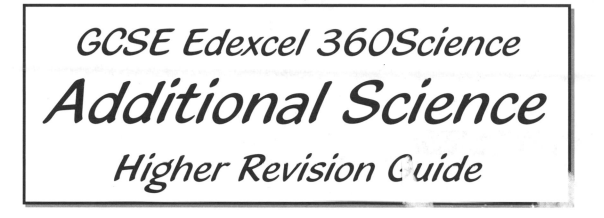

GCSE Edexcel 360Science
Additional Science
Higher Revision Guide

This book is for anyone doing **GCSE Edexcel 360Science Additional Science** at higher level.

GCSE Science is all about **understanding how science works**. And not only that — understanding it well enough to be able to **question** what you hear on TV and read in the papers.

But you can't do that without a fair chunk of **background knowledge**. Hmm, tricky.

Happily this CGP book includes all the **science facts** you need to learn, and shows you how they work in the **real world**. And in true CGP style, we've explained it all as **clearly and concisely** as possible.

It's also got some daft bits in to try and make the whole experience at least vaguely entertaining for you.

What CGP is all about

Our sole aim here at CGP is to produce the highest quality books — carefully written, immaculately presented and dangerously close to being funny.

Then we work our socks off to get them out to you — at the cheapest possible prices.

Contents

B2 TOPIC 1 — INSIDE LIVING CELLS

Respiration 1
Respiration and Exercise 2
Evaluating Health Claims 3
DNA — Making Proteins 4
Using Microorganisms 5
Revision Summary for B2 Topic 1 7

B2 TOPIC 2 — DIVIDE AND DEVELOP

Growth in Organisms 8
Cell Division — Mitosis 9
Cell Division — Meiosis 10
Stem Cells and Differentiation 11
Growth in Plants 12
Growth in Plants: Plant Hormones 13
Selective Breeding 14
Cloning and Genetic Modification 15
Gene Therapy 16
Revision Summary for B2 Topic 2 17

B2 TOPIC 3 — ENERGY FLOW

Plants and Photosynthesis 18
Rate of Photosynthesis 19
The Carbon Cycle 20
Minerals and Plants 21
The Nitrogen Cycle 22
Life on Mars 23
There's Too Many People 24
Climate Change and Food Distribution 25
Food Production 26
Revision Summary for B2 Topic 3 27

B2 TOPIC 4 — INTERDEPENDENCE

Population Sizes 28
Extreme Environments 29
Air Pollution — CO_2 and CO 30
Interpreting Data: Climate Change 31
Air Pollution — Acid Rain 32
Water Pollution 33
Living Indicators 34
Conservation 35
Recycling 36
Revision Summary for B2 Topic 4 & Answers 37

C2 TOPIC 5 — SYNTHESIS

Balancing Equations 38
Crude Oil 39
Alkanes and Alkenes 40
Cracking Hydrocarbons 41
Vegetable Oils 42
Plastics 43
Drug Synthesis 45
Relative Formula Mass 46
Empirical Formulae 47
Calculating Masses in Reactions 48
Atom Economy 49
Percentage Yield 50
Revision Summary for C2 Topic 5 51

C2 Topic 6 — In Your Element

Atoms 52
Isotopes and Relative Atomic Mass 53
The Periodic Table 54
Electron Shells 55
Ionic Bonding 56
Ionic Compounds 57
Reactivity Trends 58
Metals 59
Electrolysis and the Half-Equations 60
Revision Summary for C2 Topic 6 61

C2 Topic 7 — Chemical Structures

Covalent Bonding 62
Molecular Substances: the Halogens 63
Giant Covalent Structures: Carbon 64
Treatment and Homeopathy 65
Revision Summary for C2 Topic 7 66

C2 Topic 8 — How Fast? How Furious?

Rates of Reaction 67
Measuring Rates of Reaction 68
Collision Theory 69
Catalysts 70
Energy Transfer in Reactions 71
Reversible Reactions 72
The Haber Process 73
Revision Summary for C2 Topic 8 & Answers 74

P2 Topic 9 — As Fast As You Can

Speed and Velocity 75
Acceleration and Velocity-Time Graphs 76
Forces 77
Friction Forces and Terminal Velocity 78
Forces and Acceleration 79
Stopping Distances 81
Car Safety 82
Taking Risks 83
Revision Summary for P2 Topic 9 84

P2 Topic 10 — Roller Coasters & Relativity

Work and Kinetic Energy 85
Electrical and Potential Energy 86
Conservation of Energy 87
Power 88
Circular Motion 89
Roller Coasters 90
Einstein's Relativity 91
Revision Summary for P2 Topic 10 92

P2 Topic 11 — Putting Radiation to Use

Ionising Radiation 93
Background Radiation 94
Atomic Structure 95
Half-Life 96
Uses of Ionising Radiation 97
Radioactive Dating 98
Radioactivity Safety 99
Revision Summary for P2 Topic 11 100

P2 Topic 12 — Power of the Atom

Splitting the Atom 101
Nuclear Power 102
Nuclear Fusion 103
Static Electricity 104
Static Electricity — Examples 105
Revision Summary for P2 Topic 12 & Answers 106

Index 107

Published by Coordination Group Publications Ltd.

From original material by Richard Parsons.

Editors:
Ellen Bowness, Gemma Hallam, Ali Palin, Kate Redmond, Katherine Reed, Ami Snelling,
Julie Wakeling.

Contributors:
John Duffy, James Foster, Sandy Gardner, Jason Howell, Lucy Muncaster, John Myers,
Adrian Schmit, Moira Steven, Mike Thompson, Luke Waller.

ISBN: 978 1 84146 747 4

With thanks to Vanessa Aris, Barrie Crowther, Ian Francis and Glenn Rogers for the proofreading.
With thanks to Laura Phillips and Katie Steele for the copyright research.

With thanks to Science Photo Library for permission to reproduce the photographs used on
pages 23, 29, 35, 62 and 91.

With thanks to the Climatic Research Unit, University of East Anglia: (www.cru.uea.ac.uk)
for permission to use the data to produce the graph on page 31.

Lichen data on page 34 reproduced from "Effects of NO_x and NH_3 on lichen communities and
urban ecosystems", Imperial College. By permission of Dr Linda Davies.

With thanks to Cancer Research UK, www.cancerresearchuk.org, 2006, March to reproduce the
graph on page 33.

With thanks to Morton et al, Waste Management World for permission to reproduce the data on
page 35.

Data used to construct stopping distance diagram on page 81 from the Highway Code.
Reproduced under the terms of the Click-Use License.

Graph on page 82 based on data from "Road Casualties Great Britain 2004: Annual Report",
Department of Transport.

Groovy website: www.cgpbooks.co.uk

Printed by Elanders Hindson Ltd, Newcastle upon Tyne.
Jolly bits of clipart from CorelDRAW®

Respiration

Respiration might not sound very 'rock n roll' but it's pretty fundamental to life as we know it.
So roll up your sleeves, take a deep breath (sorry), and get stuck in...

Respiration is NOT 'Breathing In and Out'

Respiration is really important — it releases the energy that cells need to do just about everything.

1) Respiration is the process of breaking down glucose to release energy, and it goes on in every cell in your body. (Glucose contains energy in the form of chemical bonds.)

2) Respiration happens in plants too. All living things respire. It's how they get energy from their food.

This energy is used to do things like:
• build up larger molecules (like proteins)
• contract muscles (see next page)
• maintain a steady body temperature

> **RESPIRATION** is the process of **BREAKING DOWN GLUCOSE TO RELEASE ENERGY**, which goes on **IN EVERY CELL**

Aerobic Respiration Needs Plenty of Oxygen

Aerobic respiration is respiration using oxygen ('aerobic' just means 'with air'). It's the most efficient way to release energy from glucose. (You can also have anaerobic respiration, which happens without oxygen — see next page).

You need to learn the word equation for aerobic respiration:

> Glucose + Oxygen → Carbon Dioxide + Water (+ ENERGY)

Raw Materials and Waste Diffuse In and Out of Cells

1) The circulatory system carries glucose, oxygen and CO_2 around the body in the blood.

2) The glucose needed for respiration comes from breaking down food in the digestive system.

3) The oxygen comes from air breathed into the lungs. CO_2 is breathed out.

4) The smallest blood vessels in the body are the capillaries. All the cells in the body have capillaries nearby to supply them with glucose and oxygen, and to take away the waste carbon dioxide.

5) These substances move between the cells and the capillaries by a process called diffusion.

'Diffusion' is really simple. It's just the gradual movement of particles from places where there are lots of them to places where there are fewer of them. That's all it is — it's just the natural tendency for stuff to spread out. Unfortunately you also have to learn the fancy way of saying this, which is:

> **DIFFUSION** is the **MOVEMENT OF PARTICLES** from an area of **HIGHER CONCENTRATION** to an area of **LOWER CONCENTRATION**

6) When cells respire they use up oxygen and glucose, so the concentration of these inside the cells is low. The concentration of these substances in the blood is higher, so they diffuse from the capillaries into the cells.

7) When cells respire they produce lots of carbon dioxide, so the concentration of this in the cells is high. This means carbon dioxide diffuses from the cells into the blood, where the concentration is lower.

body cells
CO_2
O_2
glucose
blood capillary

Revision by diffusion — you wish...

Wouldn't that be great — if all the ideas in this book would just gradually drift across into your mind, from an area of high concentration (in the book) to an area of low concentration (in your mind — no offence). Actually, that probably will happen if you read it again. Why don't you give it a go...

Respiration and Exercise

How <u>fast</u> you respire depends on what you're doing...

When You Exercise You Respire More

1) Muscles need <u>energy</u> from respiration to <u>contract</u>. When you exercise some of your muscles contract more frequently than normal so you need <u>more energy</u>. This energy comes from <u>increased respiration</u>.

2) The increase in respiration means you need to get <u>more oxygen</u> into the cells.

3) Your <u>breathing rate increases</u> to get more oxygen into the blood, and to get this oxygenated blood around the body faster your <u>heart rate increases</u>. This <u>removes CO_2</u> more quickly at the same time.

4) To deal with the increased demand, the rate of <u>diffusion</u> of <u>carbon dioxide</u> and <u>oxygen</u> at the <u>lung surface</u> and in <u>muscle cells</u> increases.

5) When you do <u>really vigorous exercise</u> (like sprinting) your body can't supply <u>oxygen</u> to your muscles quickly enough, so they start <u>respiring anaerobically</u>.

Anaerobic Respiration Doesn't Use Oxygen At All

1) <u>Anaerobic respiration</u> happens when there's <u>not enough oxygen available</u>.

2) <u>Anaerobic</u> just means <u>without air</u> and it's <u>NOT the best way to release energy from glucose</u>.

You need to learn the overall <u>word equation</u>:

$$\text{Glucose} \rightarrow \text{Lactic Acid (+ ENERGY)}$$

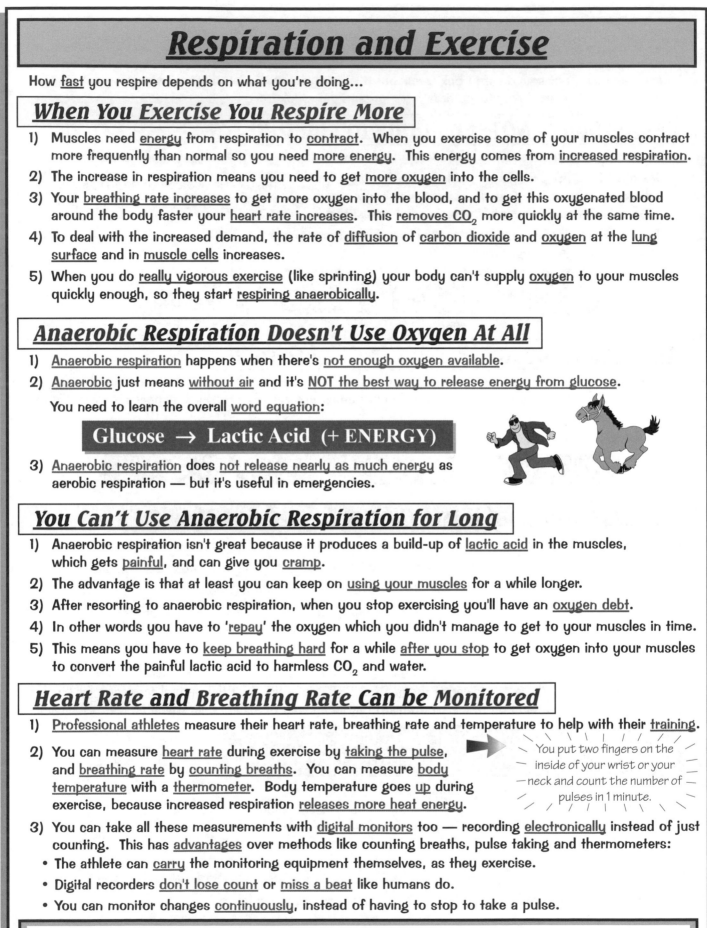

3) <u>Anaerobic respiration</u> does <u>not release nearly as much energy</u> as aerobic respiration — but it's useful in emergencies.

You Can't Use Anaerobic Respiration for Long

1) Anaerobic respiration isn't great because it produces a build-up of <u>lactic acid</u> in the muscles, which gets <u>painful</u>, and can give you <u>cramp</u>.

2) The advantage is that at least you can keep on <u>using your muscles</u> for a while longer.

3) After resorting to anaerobic respiration, when you stop exercising you'll have an <u>oxygen debt</u>.

4) In other words you have to '<u>repay</u>' the oxygen which you didn't manage to get to your muscles in time.

5) This means you have to <u>keep breathing hard</u> for a while <u>after you stop</u> to get oxygen into your muscles to convert the painful lactic acid to harmless CO_2 and water.

Heart Rate and Breathing Rate Can be Monitored

1) <u>Professional athletes</u> measure their heart rate, breathing rate and temperature to help with their <u>training</u>.

2) You can measure <u>heart rate</u> during exercise by <u>taking the pulse</u>, and <u>breathing rate</u> by <u>counting breaths</u>. You can measure <u>body temperature</u> with a <u>thermometer</u>. Body temperature goes <u>up</u> during exercise, because increased respiration <u>releases more heat energy</u>.

You put two fingers on the inside of your wrist or your neck and count the number of pulses in 1 minute.

3) You can take all these measurements with <u>digital monitors</u> too — recording <u>electronically</u> instead of just counting. This has <u>advantages</u> over methods like counting breaths, pulse taking and thermometers:
 • The athlete can <u>carry</u> the monitoring equipment themselves, as they exercise.
 • Digital recorders <u>don't lose count</u> or <u>miss a beat</u> like humans do.
 • You can monitor changes <u>continuously</u>, instead of having to stop to take a pulse.

Oxygen debt — cheap to pay back....

In the exam, you might be asked to <u>interpret data</u> on heart rates and breathing rates. If the rates go up the person is probably exercising. Don't forget that heart rate and breathing rate don't go straight back to normal when you stop exercising. Also, make sure you <u>include the units</u> — breaths/min or beats/min.

Evaluating Health Claims

Nowadays the media <u>bombard</u> you with a variety of <u>new diets</u> and exercise regimes almost every day. How do you tell the plums from the turkeys?

Not All Diets are Scientifically Proven

With each new day comes a new celebrity-endorsed <u>weight-loss</u> or <u>healthy-eating diet</u>. It's a wonder anyone's overweight or eating unhealthily.

1) A common way to promote a new <u>diet</u> is to say, "Celebrity A has lost x pounds using it" or "Celebrity A feels so much better now she follows the 'CGP liver and sprouts galore' diet".

2) But effectiveness in <u>one person</u> doesn't mean much. Only a <u>large survey</u> can tell if a weight-loss diet is more or less effective than just <u>eating less</u> and <u>exercising more</u> — and these aren't done often. Also, only a large survey can tell if a supposed healthy-eating diet is really <u>good for you</u>.

3) The <u>Atkins weight-loss diet</u> was high profile, and controversial — so it got investigated. People on the diet certainly lost weight. But the diet's effect on general health (especially <u>long-term</u> health) has been questioned. The jury's still out.

4) It's not easy to decide what to <u>believe</u> and what to <u>ignore</u>. But these things are worth looking for:

> a) Is the report a <u>scientific</u> study, published in a <u>reputable</u> journal?
> b) Was it written by a <u>qualified</u> person (not connected with the food producers)?
> c) Was the <u>sample</u> of people asked/tested large enough to give <u>valid results</u>?
> d) Have there been <u>other studies</u> which found similar results?

A 'yes' to one or more of these is a good sign.

Official Advice is Based on Scientific Evidence

1) The UK government says that a healthy diet should contain lots of <u>fruit</u> and <u>vegetables</u>, <u>starchy foods</u> like pasta and rice, and some <u>protein</u>. They recommend that you eat at least <u>five portions</u> of different fruit and veg a day. It also recommends cutting down on saturated and trans <u>fats</u>, <u>salt</u> and <u>refined sugars</u> (e.g. those found in sweets).

2) This advice is based on scientific evidence from many <u>surveys</u> and <u>studies</u> done by reputable institutions, including the <u>NHS</u>, the <u>British Heart Foundation</u>, the <u>Food Standards Agency</u> and the <u>Department for Environment, Food and Rural Affairs (DEFRA)</u>.

3) Every now and again a <u>new study</u> comes up with something not found before. If more studies find the same thing and scientists agree with each other the <u>advice is altered</u> to <u>include the results</u>. For example, official advice used to be to reduce the amount of <u>fat</u> in your diet as much as possible as all fat was thought to be bad for you. Now scientists realise that <u>some types</u> of fat are actually good for you, so the guidelines have been changed to recommend just reducing the amount of 'bad' fats.

Official Advice on Exercise is Also Based on Scientific Evidence

1) The current UK government recommendation is to exercise for at least <u>30</u> minutes, <u>five times</u> a week in order to stay fit and healthy.

2) Not so long ago the recommendation was <u>20</u> minutes, <u>three times</u> a week.

3) The advice was changed after a report published in 2004 suggested that this new level of exercise could cut an individual's <u>risk</u> of <u>heart disease</u> by up to <u>50%</u> (compared with the previous recommendation). It also reduced the risk of stroke and type 2 diabetes.

100% of people said eating CGP books helped them lose weight*

Sometimes official advice is criticised for being <u>behind the times</u> as governments are often very <u>cautious</u> when making their recommendations. Some things that scientists look for when studying effects of diets and exercise regimes are blood cholesterol levels, fitness levels, vitamin levels and mineral levels.

DNA — Making Proteins

Your DNA is basically a long list of instructions on how to make all the proteins in your body.

DNA — a Double Helix of Paired Bases

1) A DNA molecule has two strands coiled together in the shape of a double helix (two spirals), as shown in the diagram opposite.

2) The two strands are held together by chemicals called bases. There are four different bases (shown in the diagram as different colours) — adenine (A), cytosine (C), guanine (G) and thymine (T).

3) The bases are paired, and they always pair up in the same way — it's always A-T and C-G. This is called base-pairing.

Adenine   Thymine

Guanine   Cytosine

A Gene Codes for a Specific Protein

1) A gene is a section of DNA. It contains the instructions to make a specific protein.

2) Cells make proteins by stringing amino acids together in a particular order.

3) Only 20 different amino acids are used to make up thousands of different proteins.

4) The order of the bases in a gene simply tells cells in what order to put the amino acids together:

> Each set of three bases (called a triplet) codes for a particular amino acid.
> Here's an example (don't worry — you don't have to remember the specific codes):
> TAT codes for tyrosine and GCA for alanine. If the order of the bases in the gene is
> TAT-GCA-TAT then the order of amino acids in the protein will be tyrosine-alanine-tyrosine.

5) DNA also determines which genes are switched on or off — and so which proteins the cell produces, e.g. haemoglobin or keratin. That in turn determines what type of cell it is, e.g. red blood cell, skin cell.

6) Some of the proteins help to make all the other things that aren't made of protein (like cell membranes) from substances that come from your diet (like fats and minerals).

Proteins are Made by Ribosomes

Proteins are made in the cell by organelles called ribosomes. DNA is found in the cell nucleus and can't move out of it because it's really big. The cell needs to get the information from the DNA to the ribosome in the cell cytoplasm. This is done using a molecule called RNA, which is very similar to DNA, but it's much shorter and only a single strand. RNA is like a messenger between the DNA in the nucleus and the ribosome. Here's how it's done:

RNA molecule forming

1) The two DNA strands unzip. A molecule of RNA is made using the DNA as a template. Base pairing ensures it's an exact match.

2) The RNA molecule moves out of the nucleus and joins with a ribosome.

3) The job of the ribosome is to stick amino acids together in a chain to make a polypeptide (protein), following the order of bases in the RNA.

ribosome

RNA

protein   amino acids

What do DNA and a game of rounders have in common?

...they both have four bases. The order of bases determines what amino acid is added and the order of amino acids determines the type of protein. All the enzymes in your body are proteins, as are your hair and your nails. Enzymes control many processes that make non-protein things.

Using Microorganisms

Microorganisms (like bacteria) are also made of <u>cells</u> containing <u>genetic material</u>. They reproduce very quickly and are <u>easy to grow and manipulate</u>. This makes them useful to humans...

Microorganisms Produce Useful By-Products

Like all other living things, microorganisms <u>respire</u> (see pages 1-2). They use an <u>external food source</u> (usually a sugar) to get their <u>energy</u>. The breakdown of sugars into simpler molecules is often called <u>fermentation</u>. Microorganisms can respire <u>aerobically</u> or <u>anaerobically</u>.

1) <u>Aerobic respiration</u> produces <u>carbon dioxide</u> as a <u>by-product</u>. <u>Yeast</u>, used in making <u>bread</u>, respire aerobically — the CO_2 produced makes the bread rise.

2) Many bacteria can respire <u>anaerobically</u> to make <u>lactic acid</u>. Bacteria are added to milk to make <u>cheese</u> — they convert the <u>lactose sugar</u> in the milk into <u>lactic acid</u>, which acidifies the milk. The milk <u>curdles</u> to form cheese.

Some Medicines Come from Microorganisms

Antibiotics

<u>Antibiotics</u> are used to <u>destroy</u> (or stop from growing) <u>bacteria</u> which cause <u>disease</u>. Antibiotics are the product of microorganisms. E.g.

- <u>Penicillin</u> is an antibiotic made by growing <u>mould</u> in a fermenter (see next page).
- The mould is grown in a liquid culture medium containing <u>sugar</u> and other nutrients (for example, a source of <u>nitrogen</u> to help make proteins). The sugar is used up as the mould grows.

Human Proteins

1) Microorganisms can be <u>genetically engineered</u> to make medicines.

2) Some human diseases are caused by <u>lack</u> of a <u>working protein</u>, e.g. people with type 1 diabetes can't produce the protein insulin.

3) The <u>gene</u> coding for the <u>working protein</u> can be taken from a healthy human and put into a microorganism.

4) The microorganisms are then <u>grown</u> in <u>fermenters</u>. They produce large amounts of the protein, which can be taken by the sufferer to treat the disease.

Microorganisms are used to make human insulin to treat diabetes

- The human insulin gene is 'cut' from human DNA using <u>enzymes</u>. Enzymes are also used to <u>cut the DNA</u> of the bacteria and then to <u>insert</u> the useful gene.
- The bacteria are then <u>cultivated</u> (grown) and soon there are millions of identical bacteria all producing human insulin. This is <u>purified</u> and used to <u>treat sufferers</u>.
- Before genetic engineering, diabetics had to use insulin extracted from the pancreases of slaughtered <u>pigs</u> and <u>cows</u>. The insulin was slightly different from the human form and so wasn't as <u>effective</u>. It also sometimes caused <u>allergic reactions</u>... not good.

Insulin gene → enzymes cut the gene out → DNA of Bacteria
Human DNA → enzymes cut it ... → ...and then they insert the human DNA
the bacteria are then grown like mad... → Insulin

Soon they will take over the world...

So, all in all microorganisms are pretty useful things. Genetically engineered microorganisms are also being used to make clotting factors to treat <u>haemophilia</u> (a blood clotting disorder).

Using Microorganisms

There are plenty of reasons why we use <u>microorganisms</u> to make things like lactic acid and alcohol (rather than making them in a chemical factory, say).

Mycoprotein — Food from Fungi

1) Mycoprotein is used to make <u>meat substitutes</u> for <u>vegetarian</u> meals, e.g. <u>Quorn</u>.
2) The fungus is grown in <u>fermenters</u>, using <u>glucose syrup</u> as food.
3) The fungus respires <u>aerobically</u>, so it needs to be supplied with oxygen.

Mycoprotein isn't a by-product — it's actually the squished fungi. Eeew...

Advantages of Using Microorganisms for Food Production

1) Microorganisms like bacteria and fungi can <u>grow very quickly</u>. They can grow miles quicker than plants or animals... which is good if you're using them to make food.
2) They're also <u>easy to look after</u>. All that's needed is <u>something to grow them in</u>, <u>food</u>, <u>oxygen</u>, and the <u>right temperature</u>.
3) Another plus is that food can be produced whether the <u>climate is hot or cold</u>. Many places in the world are pretty unsuitable for farming crops or animals, e.g. Siberia, parts of Africa and Outer Mongolia. Microorganisms can be used to produce food anywhere if you have the right equipment.
4) <u>Microorganisms</u> can use <u>waste products</u> from <u>agriculture</u> and <u>industry</u> as <u>food</u> for their life processes.
5) This often makes using microorganisms <u>cheaper</u> than other methods.

Microorganisms are Grown in Fermenters on a Large Scale

A fermenter is a big container full of <u>liquid</u> 'culture medium' which microorganisms can <u>grow</u> and <u>reproduce</u> in. The fermenter needs to have the <u>right conditions</u> for the microorganisms to <u>grow</u> and produce their <u>useful product</u>.

1) <u>Food</u> is provided in the liquid culture medium. Microorganisms need <u>carbohydrates</u> (sugars) as an energy source, plus <u>mineral ions</u>, and sometimes <u>nitrates</u> (to make protein) and <u>vitamins</u>. More nutrients can be pumped in if needed.
2) Air is piped in to supply <u>oxygen</u> to the microorganisms (if they respire aerobically).
3) The microorganisms need to be kept at the <u>right temperature</u> for optimum growth. If it's <u>too cold</u> the growth rate will <u>slow down</u>. If it's <u>too hot</u> enzymes in the microorganisms will be denatured (destroyed) and growth will stop. The microorganisms produce <u>heat</u> by respiration, so the fermenters must be <u>cooled</u>. This is usually done with a <u>water</u> jacket which cold water is pumped through.

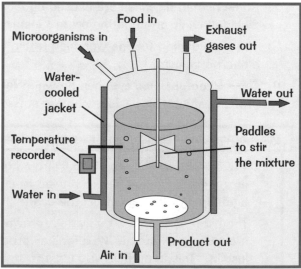

4) The <u>right pH</u> is needed for the microorganisms to thrive. Instruments will monitor this.
5) <u>Sterile (aseptic) conditions</u> are needed to <u>prevent contamination</u> from other microorganisms.
6) The microorganisms need to be kept from <u>sinking to the bottom</u>. A <u>motorised stirrer</u> keeps them moving around and maintains an even temperature.

Culture medium — sounds very BBC Four to me...

Fermenters come in all shapes and sizes — the industrial ones can contain as much volume as a swimming pool. Anyway, all you need to do now is learn the facts on this page and do the revision questions on the next page. Then Topic 1 will be completely <u>done and dusted</u>.

Revision Summary for B2 Topic 1

Hurrah. The first section is almost complete. Before you move on to Topic 2, try these revision questions. Do them all and check your answers. If you get any wrong, then learn those bits again, and do the questions again. Keep on going until you can get all the questions right. It's a hard slog, but you've got to do it. Otherwise all the useful facts you've just read will float away... and you'll be left with nothing but a vague mental image of a fermenter.

1) Which of the following statements are true? (You can pick more than one.)
   a) Respiration is breathing in and out.
   b) Carbon dioxide is a product of aerobic respiration.
   c) Respiration only happens in animals.

2) Write down the word equation for aerobic respiration.

3) What is diffusion?

4) Write down the word equation for anaerobic respiration.

5) Give one advantage and one disadvantage of anaerobic respiration.

6)* Danny measured his heart rate before, during and after exercise. He plotted a graph of the results. Look at the graph and then answer the three questions below.

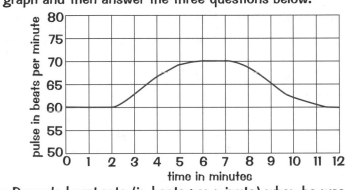

   a) What was Danny's heart rate (in beats per minute) when he was at rest?
   b) After how many minutes did Danny start exercising?
   c) What was Danny's highest heart rate?

7) Give three advantages of using a digital monitor to record breathing rate.

8) Are all weight-loss diets scientifically proven?

9) How much exercise does the UK government recommend you do per week? Why has this recommendation changed in recent years?

10) What shape is a DNA molecule?

11) Name the four different bases in DNA. How do they pair up?

12) What is a gene?

13) What does a triplet of three bases code for?

14) How does the DNA in a cell determine which proteins are produced by that cell?

15) What is a polypeptide?

16) Describe the stages of protein synthesis.

17) How does yeast make bread rise?

18) How do bacteria convert milk into cheese?

19) Give an example of an antibiotic.

20) Describe how microorganisms are used to produce human insulin.

21) What is mycoprotein used for?

22) Write down five advantages of using microorganisms for food production.

23) What is a fermenter? Give five features of a typical fermenter.

24) Why are aseptic (sterile) conditions necessary in a fermenter?

* Answer on page 37

Growth in Organisms

This topic's about <u>growth and development</u> in plants and animals. Organisms grow using a combination of cell division, cell elongation and cell differentiation — which you'll learn all about in exquisite detail as you go through the topic. But first, here's a bit of general stuff about growth...

Growth is an Increase in Size or Weight

You can <u>measure</u> the <u>growth</u> of an organism in these three ways:

1) **Size** — You can measure its <u>height</u>, <u>length</u>, <u>width</u> or <u>circumference</u>.

2) **Wet weight** — Organisms <u>contain</u> a lot of <u>water</u>. The weight of the organism depends on how much water it has gained or lost (e.g. through drinking or sweating). The <u>wet weight</u> of the organism is its weight <u>including all the water</u> in its body — it can vary a lot from <u>one day to the next</u>.

3) **Dry weight** — The <u>dry weight</u> is the weight of an organism with <u>no water in its body</u>. This doesn't vary in the same way as wet weight, but you can only measure it once the organism's dead. The dead organism is <u>dried out</u> by leaving it in a hot oven overnight — then what's left is weighed.

Organisms of the Same Species Vary in Size

1) <u>Individual organisms</u> of the same species <u>vary</u> in <u>size</u> — e.g. humans aren't all the same height.

2) But each species has a <u>range of sizes</u> which <u>most individuals</u> fall within — e.g. most adult humans are between 4' 8" and 6' 8" in height. It's very unusual for a human to grow to 8 foot tall.

3) When individuals within a species have a characteristic which <u>varies along a range</u> like this, it is called <u>continuous variation</u>. <u>Size</u> (e.g. height, width, weight) is an example of a characteristic showing continuous variation.

4) Several <u>factors</u> affect how individual organisms <u>grow</u> and what <u>size</u> they become. For example, how tall humans grow is influenced by their <u>genes</u>, <u>hormones</u> and <u>diet</u>.

Some Animals are Able to Regenerate

1) A few animals have the ability to <u>regrow</u> (regenerate) part of their body if it is <u>damaged</u>:

- If some types of <u>worm</u> are cut in two, the front part can grow a new 'tail'.
- If a <u>young spider</u> loses a leg, it can grow a new one (adult spiders can't, though).
- Some <u>reptiles</u>, like lizards, can regrow a lost leg or tail.

2) The ability to regenerate parts of the body is <u>pretty rare</u> though. It tends to happen in fairly simple (or very young) animals which still contain lots of <u>stem cells</u> (see p.11).

Growth Factors Can be Used to Enhance Performance in Sport

1) Growth factors are chemicals which <u>stimulate</u> the <u>body</u> to <u>grow</u> and to make <u>extra muscle</u>.

2) Some athletes have used growth factor drugs to <u>improve their performance</u> at <u>sport</u>. This is <u>illegal</u> because it gives them an <u>unfair advantage</u> over other competitors. It also has health risks:

- Growth factor drugs can have <u>bad side effects</u> for health: they can <u>reduce fertility</u>, can increase the risk of <u>heart disease</u> and can sometimes trigger mental illnesses like <u>depression</u>.
- Some growth factors cause <u>women</u> to develop <u>male characteristics</u>, e.g. a deeper voice.

3) <u>Athletes</u> are given <u>random tests</u> for growth factor drugs.

Growth — birds do it, bees do it, even educated fleas do it...

This is an <u>evil page</u>. It lulls you into a false sense of security at the beginning by saying nice, easy things like 'growth is an increase in size'. But then it does a <u>sucker punch</u> — suddenly bringing in loads of tricky ideas like dry weight, continuous variation, and regeneration... Ouch.

Cell Division — Mitosis

The cells of your body <u>divide</u> to <u>produce more cells</u>. This is so that your body can grow and repair damaged cells. Of course, cell division doesn't just happen in humans — animals and plants do it too.

Mitosis Makes New Cells for Growth and Repair

1) <u>Human body cells</u> are <u>diploid</u>. This means they have <u>two versions</u> of each <u>chromosome</u> — one from the person's <u>mother</u>, and one from their <u>father</u>. This diagram shows the <u>23 pairs of chromosomes</u> in a human cell.

2) When a cell <u>divides</u> it makes <u>two</u> cells <u>identical</u> to the original cell — each with a <u>nucleus</u> containing the <u>same number</u> of chromosomes as the original cell.

3) This type of cell division is called <u>mitosis</u>. It's used when humans (and animals and plants) want to <u>grow</u> or to <u>replace</u> cells that have been <u>damaged</u>.

Mitosis Results in Two Identical Cells

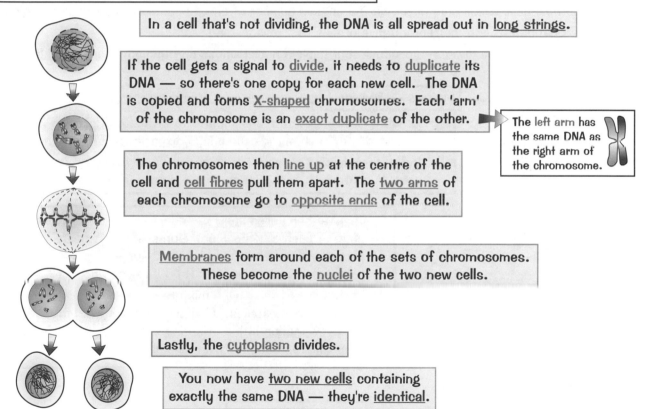

In a cell that's not dividing, the DNA is all spread out in <u>long strings</u>.

If the cell gets a signal to <u>divide</u>, it needs to <u>duplicate</u> its DNA — so there's one copy for each new cell. The DNA is copied and forms <u>X-shaped</u> chromosomes. Each 'arm' of the chromosome is an <u>exact duplicate</u> of the other.

The left arm has the same DNA as the right arm of the chromosome.

The chromosomes then <u>line up</u> at the centre of the cell and <u>cell fibres</u> pull them apart. The <u>two arms</u> of each chromosome go to <u>opposite ends</u> of the cell.

<u>Membranes</u> form around each of the sets of chromosomes. These become the <u>nuclei</u> of the two new cells.

Lastly, the <u>cytoplasm</u> divides.

You now have <u>two new cells</u> containing exactly the same DNA — they're <u>identical</u>.

Most Cells Can Only Divide a Limited Number of Times

1) Most cells have a <u>limit</u> to the <u>number</u> of times they can <u>divide</u>. This is called the <u>Hayflick limit</u>.

2) After they reach this limit, the cell <u>stops dividing</u>. The human limit is about 52 divisions, but most never reach this number.

3) <u>Stem cells</u> (see page 11) and <u>cancer cells</u> have <u>no</u> Hayflick limit — they can divide as many times as they want to. This is what makes cancer cells dangerous — they continue growing uncontrollably and form <u>tumours</u>.

Now that I have your undivided attention...

The next page is about meiosis, which is quite similar to mitosis. It's easy to get them confused if you're not careful. So make sure you've <u>learnt mitosis really thoroughly</u>, before moving on. The best way to do this is to: 1) learn the diagram on this page, 2) cover it over, 3) sketch it out.

Cell Division — Meiosis

You thought mitosis was exciting. Hah. You ain't seen nothing yet.

Gametes Have Half the Usual Number of Chromosomes

1) <u>Gametes</u> are 'sex cells'. They're called <u>ova</u> (single, ovum) in females, and <u>sperm</u> in males. During <u>sexual reproduction</u>, two <u>gametes combine</u> to form a <u>new cell</u> which will grow to become a new organism.

2) <u>Gametes</u> are <u>haploid</u> — this means they only have <u>one copy</u> of each <u>chromosome</u>. This is so that when <u>two gametes combine</u> in sexual reproduction, the resulting cell (zygote) has the <u>right number of chromosomes</u>.

3) For example, human body cells have <u>46 chromosomes</u>. The <u>gametes</u> have <u>23 chromosomes each</u>, so that when an egg and sperm combine, you get 46 chromosomes again.

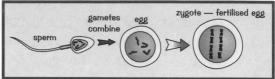

Meiosis Involves Two Divisions

1) To make new cells which only have <u>half</u> the original number of chromosomes, cells divide by <u>meiosis</u>.

2) Meiosis <u>only</u> happens in the <u>reproductive organs</u> (e.g. ovaries and testes).

3) <u>Meiosis</u> is when a cell divides to produce <u>four haploid nuclei</u> whose <u>chromosomes are NOT identical</u>.

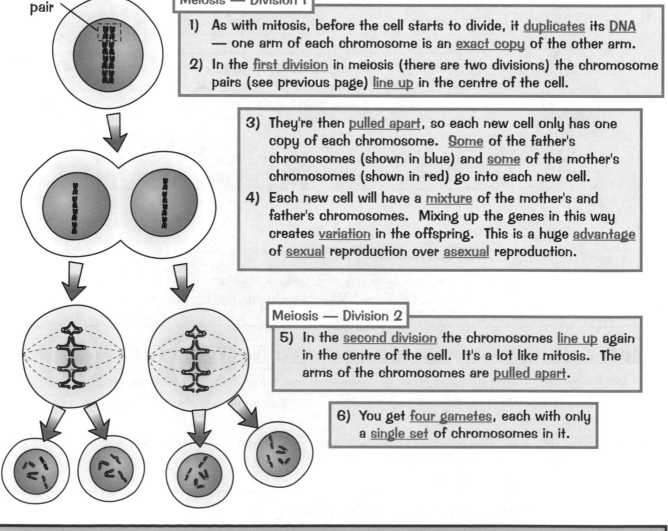

chromosome pair

Meiosis — Division 1

1) As with mitosis, before the cell starts to divide, it <u>duplicates</u> its <u>DNA</u> — one arm of each chromosome is an <u>exact copy</u> of the other arm.

2) In the <u>first division</u> in meiosis (there are two divisions) the chromosome pairs (see previous page) <u>line up</u> in the centre of the cell.

3) They're then <u>pulled apart</u>, so each new cell only has one copy of each chromosome. <u>Some</u> of the father's chromosomes (shown in blue) and <u>some</u> of the mother's chromosomes (shown in red) go into each new cell.

4) Each new cell will have a <u>mixture</u> of the mother's and father's chromosomes. Mixing up the genes in this way creates <u>variation</u> in the offspring. This is a huge <u>advantage</u> of <u>sexual</u> reproduction over <u>asexual</u> reproduction.

Meiosis — Division 2

5) In the <u>second division</u> the chromosomes <u>line up</u> again in the centre of the cell. It's a lot like mitosis. The arms of the chromosomes are <u>pulled apart</u>.

6) You get <u>four gametes</u>, each with only a <u>single set</u> of chromosomes in it.

Relegation to the Second Division is inevitable...

Again, the best thing to do is to <u>learn the diagram</u>. Cover it up and sketch it out.

Stem Cells and Differentiation

Cells divide to make you grow. They also <u>differentiate</u> (specialise) so they can do different jobs.

Embryonic Stem Cells Can Turn into Any Type of Cell

1) A fertilised egg can divide by mitosis to produce a bundle of cells — the <u>embryo</u> of the new organism.

2) To start with, the <u>cells</u> in the embryo are <u>all the same</u> (<u>undifferentiated</u>). They are called <u>embryonic stem cells</u>.

3) Stem cells are <u>able to divide</u> to produce either more stem cells or <u>different types</u> of <u>specialised cell</u> (e.g. blood cells).

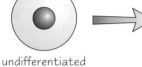

undifferentiated stem cell

differentiated white blood cell

4) The process of stem cells <u>becoming specialised</u> is called <u>differentiation</u>. It is by this process that the embryo starts to develop a recognisably human body with <u>organs</u> and <u>systems</u>.

5) <u>Adult</u> humans only have <u>stem cells</u> in certain places like the <u>bone marrow</u>. These stem cells <u>aren't as versatile</u> as the stem cells in embryos — they can only differentiate into certain types of cell.

Stem Cells May be Able to Cure Many Diseases

1) Doctors already use <u>adult stem cells</u> to cure some <u>diseases</u>. E.g., <u>sickle cell anaemia</u> can sometimes be cured with a <u>bone marrow transplant</u> (containing adult stem cells which produce new blood cells).

2) Scientists have experimented with <u>extracting stem cells</u> from very early <u>human embryos</u> and <u>growing</u> them. Under certain conditions the stem cells will differentiate into <u>specialised cells</u>.

3) It <u>might</u> be possible to use stem cells to create specialised cells to <u>replace</u> those which have been <u>damaged</u> by <u>disease</u> or <u>injury</u>, e.g. new cardiac muscle cells to help someone with heart disease. This <u>potential</u> for <u>new cures</u> is the reason for the huge scientific interest in stem cells.

4) Before this can happen, a lot of <u>research</u> needs to be done — and there are <u>ethical concerns</u> about this:

- Some people are strongly <u>against</u> embryonic stem cell research. They argue that human embryos <u>shouldn't</u> be used for experiments because each one is a <u>potential human life</u>. They say that scientists should find <u>other sources of stem cells</u>.

- Other people think that the aim of <u>curing patients</u> who are <u>suffering</u> should be <u>more important</u> than the potential life of the embryos. They point out that the embryos used are often <u>unwanted ones</u> from <u>fertility clinics</u> — if they weren't used for research, they would probably be <u>destroyed</u>.

- In some countries stem cell research is <u>banned</u>. It's allowed in the UK under <u>strict guidelines</u>.

A Pregnancy Can Legally be Terminated Up to 24 Weeks

After the 8th week of pregnancy, the embryo starts to look a bit more human and is called a <u>foetus</u>. In Britain, a <u>termination</u> (induced abortion) is <u>legal</u> until a <u>foetus is 24 weeks old</u> if <u>two doctors</u> agree that termination is necessary. An abortion can be carried out later than this if the pregnancy is putting the <u>mother's health at serious risk</u> or if there is a major <u>foetal abnormality</u>. The 24-week limit came into effect in <u>1991</u> — <u>24 weeks</u> is the age at which a <u>foetus</u> can <u>usually survive</u> (with medical help) outside the womb.

1) Some people argue that abortion at any stage of pregnancy is <u>unethical</u>. They argue that <u>human life</u> starts at <u>fertilisation</u> — and ending pregnancy is the same as <u>killing a human being</u>.

2) Other people argue that the foetus doesn't <u>become human</u> until it is <u>conscious</u> — for example, when it starts <u>feeling pain</u>. They argue that abortion should be allowed up until this point.

3) But it's difficult to pinpoint exactly when the foetus becomes conscious and can feel pain. Some people argue that it's the point when <u>pain receptors</u> first develop at about <u>7 weeks</u>. Others argue that the foetus can't feel pain until the pain receptors are <u>connected up in the foetus' brain</u> — which doesn't happen until about <u>26 weeks</u>.

This page is an ethical minefield...

These topics often <u>make people feel emotional</u>. Which isn't the best mindset for scientific thought...

Growth in Plants

Plant growth is different from animal growth — plants can <u>regenerate</u> (grow back if they're damaged) and many of them <u>grow almost continuously.</u>

6 Factors Affect the Growth and Distribution of Plants

In order to grow, plants need to be able to <u>photosynthesise</u> (use the Sun's energy to make glucose) and <u>respire</u> (break down glucose to release energy). They also need <u>nutrients</u> from the soil.

(1) **Soil nutrients**

The <u>soil</u> contains <u>nutrients</u> essential for plant growth. E.g. <u>nitrates</u> are used by plants to make proteins. <u>Phosphates</u> have a role in the reactions for photosynthesis and respiration. <u>Magnesium</u> is needed for making chlorophyll.

(2) **Light**

Plants need <u>sunlight</u> for <u>photosynthesis</u> (see p.18). Without sunlight, plants can't photosynthesise and don't get the glucose they need for energy and growth.

(3) **Temperature**

Plants grow best when it's <u>warm</u>, but not too hot. The reactions for photosynthesis and respiration happen quicker in warmer temperatures — so the rate of growth increases. But if it gets <u>too hot</u>, then enzymes (p.70) involved in the reactions will be destroyed and growth stops.

(4) **Carbon dioxide**

There's only a small amount of carbon dioxide (CO_2) in the air — about 0.04%. Plants need CO_2 for <u>photosynthesis</u>. If there isn't enough, plant growth slows down.

(5) **Oxygen**

Plants need oxygen for <u>respiration</u> (which provides energy for growth). Plants absorb oxygen from the atmosphere and also create it as a by-product of photosynthesis.

(6) **Plant hormones**

Plant hormones can <u>stimulate growth</u>. There's more about them on the next page.

Some Plants Can Grow in Poor Conditions

Some environments <u>aren't perfect</u> for plant growth. Plants that grow in these areas will often be <u>specially adapted</u> to be able to survive in the poor conditions. E.g.

Environment	Conditions	Specially adapted plant
Sand dunes	Poor soil containing little water.	Marram grass — has curled up leaves to reduce water loss.
Woodland	Low light intensity — trees overshadow smaller plants.	Bluebell — stores food over winter, so that it can grow quickly in spring, before the trees are in leaf.
Pond	Water may make oxygen and carbon dioxide exchange difficult.	Water lily — has all its holes (stomata) for oxygen and carbon dioxide exchange on the top surfaces of its leaves.

Other plants might not be able to survive in these conditions — so there's less competition for nutrients, light etc.

Plants need a place in the Sun — next to the TV listings perhaps...

'<u>Distribution of plants</u>' means the number of plants growing in different areas. In areas with good conditions, more plants will grow. In areas with poor conditions, usually only adapted plants will grow.

Growth in Plants: Plant Hormones

Plants <u>don't</u> grow randomly. Plant hormones make sure they grow in a <u>useful direction</u> (e.g. towards light).

Auxins are Plant Growth Hormones

1) <u>Auxins</u> are <u>plant hormones</u> which control <u>growth</u> near the <u>tips</u> of <u>shoots</u> and <u>roots</u>.
2) Auxin is produced in the <u>tips</u> and <u>diffuses backwards</u> to stimulate the <u>cell elongation (enlargement) process</u> which occurs in the cells <u>just behind</u> the tips.
3) If the tip of a shoot is <u>removed</u>, no auxin is available and the shoot may <u>stop growing</u>.
4) Auxins are involved in the responses of plants to <u>light</u>, <u>gravity</u> and <u>water</u>.

Auxins Change the Direction of Root and Shoot Growth

Extra auxin <u>promotes</u> growth in the <u>shoot</u> but actually <u>inhibits</u> growth in the <u>root</u> — but this produces the <u>desired result</u> in <u>both cases</u>.

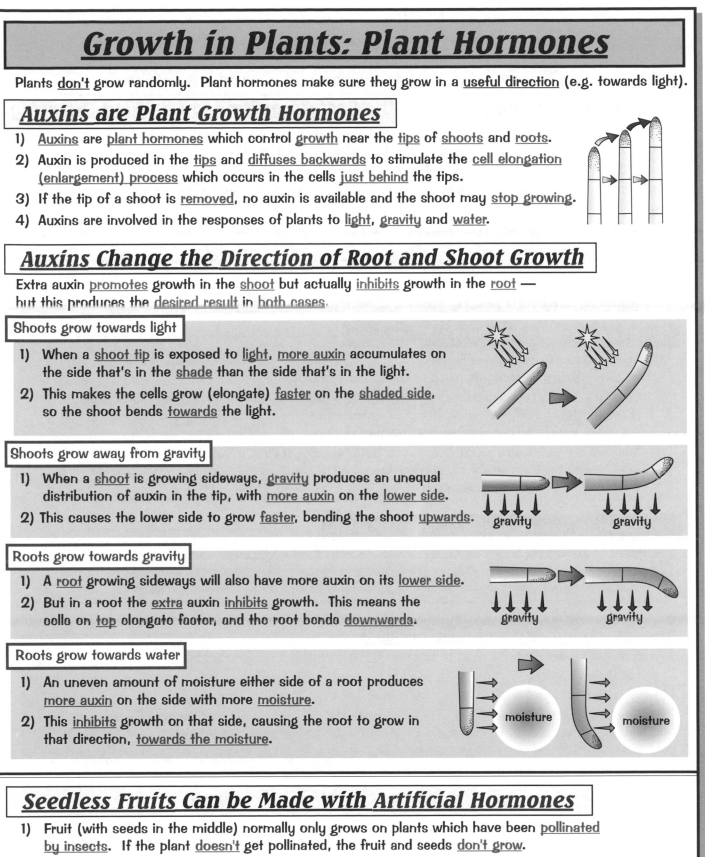

Shoots grow towards light

1) When a <u>shoot tip</u> is exposed to <u>light</u>, <u>more auxin</u> accumulates on the side that's in the <u>shade</u> than the side that's in the light.
2) This makes the cells grow (elongate) <u>faster</u> on the <u>shaded side</u>, so the shoot bends <u>towards</u> the light.

Shoots grow away from gravity

1) When a <u>shoot</u> is growing sideways, <u>gravity</u> produces an unequal distribution of auxin in the tip, with <u>more auxin</u> on the <u>lower side</u>.
2) This causes the lower side to grow <u>faster</u>, bending the shoot <u>upwards</u>.

Roots grow towards gravity

1) A <u>root</u> growing sideways will also have more auxin on its <u>lower side</u>.
2) But in a root the <u>extra</u> auxin <u>inhibits</u> growth. This means the cells on <u>top</u> elongate faster, and the root bends <u>downwards</u>.

Roots grow towards water

1) An uneven amount of moisture either side of a root produces <u>more auxin</u> on the side with more <u>moisture</u>.
2) This <u>inhibits</u> growth on that side, causing the root to grow in that direction, <u>towards the moisture</u>.

Seedless Fruits Can be Made with Artificial Hormones

1) Fruit (with seeds in the middle) normally only grows on plants which have been <u>pollinated by insects</u>. If the plant <u>doesn't</u> get pollinated, the fruit and seeds <u>don't grow</u>.
2) If <u>growth hormones</u> are applied to the <u>unpollinated flowers</u> of some types of plant, the <u>fruit will grow</u> but the <u>seeds won't</u>. Some <u>seedless citrus fruits</u> can be grown this way.
3) <u>Hormones</u> are also used in the production of <u>seedless grapes</u> (although these are usually fertilised first).

A plant auxin to a bar — 'ouch'...

Learn the page. Learn the <u>whole darn page</u>. There's no getting out of it folks.

Selective Breeding

Selective breeding is a way for humans to develop crops/herds with <u>useful characteristics</u>.

Selective Breeding is Mating the Best Organisms to Get Good Offspring

<u>Selective breeding</u> is when humans select the plants or animals that are going to breed and flourish, according to what <u>we</u> want from them. It's also called <u>artificial selection</u>.

This is the basic process involved in selective breeding:

1) From the existing stock, the organisms which have the <u>best characteristics</u> are selected.
2) They're <u>bred</u> with each other.
3) The <u>best</u> of the <u>offspring</u> are selected and <u>bred</u>.
4) This process is repeated over several generations to develop the <u>desired traits</u>.

Selective Breeding is Very Useful in Farming

Farmers can improve the quality of milk from cattle

1) Cows can be selectively bred to produce offspring with particular characteristics, e.g. a <u>high milk yield</u> or <u>milk high in nutrients</u> (such as calcium or protein).

2) Cows are usually impregnated using <u>artificial insemination</u>. Semen from a <u>bull</u> which has <u>good characteristics</u> (or whose mother had good characteristics — bulls obviously don't produce milk) is used to artificially inseminate a <u>large number of cows</u>.

3) A typical dairy cow now produces between <u>5000 and 6000 litres</u> of milk a year. This is much more than dairy cows produced a hundred years ago. This is partly because of selective breeding and partly due to <u>intensive farming methods</u> (e.g. giving cows a special diet).

Farmers can increase the number of offspring in sheep

Farmers can selectively breed <u>sheep</u> to <u>increase</u> the number of <u>lambs born</u>. Female sheep (ewes) who produce large numbers of offspring are bred with rams whose mothers had large numbers of offspring. The <u>characteristic</u> of having large numbers of offspring is <u>passed on</u> to the next generation.

Farmers can increase the yield from dwarf wheat

1) Selective breeding can be used to combine <u>two different desirable characteristics</u>.

2) <u>Tall wheat plants</u> have a good grain yield but are easily damaged by wind and rain. <u>Dwarf wheat plants</u> can resist wind and rain but have a lower grain yield.

3) These two types of wheat plant were <u>cross-bred</u>, and the best resulting wheat plants were cross-bred again. This resulted in a <u>new variety</u> of wheat <u>combining the good characteristics</u> — dwarf wheat plants which could <u>resist bad weather</u> and had a <u>high grain yield</u>.

There are Disadvantages to Selective Breeding

1) Only some of the original population is bred from — so there's <u>less variety</u> in the <u>gene pool</u> of the organisms. All the organisms in a crop/herd will be <u>closely related</u> and have <u>similar characteristics</u> — including their <u>level of disease-resistance</u>. Some diseases might be able to <u>wipe out</u> the whole lot.

2) Some of the characteristics encouraged by selective breeding are <u>beneficial for humans</u>, but <u>not</u> for the <u>organisms</u> themselves. E.g. selective breeding to <u>increase milk yields</u> means cows produce more milk than they would need to feed a calf. They often suffer from <u>mastitis</u> (inflammation of the udders).

I use the same genes all the time too — they flatter my hips...

Selective breeding can be used to nurture all sorts of characteristics — high yield, fast growth, ability to survive in a tough environment, resistance to a particular disease...

Cloning and Genetic Modification

There are two different things on this page — don't get them confused. Cloning is using an organism's DNA to create a genetically identical new organism. Genetic modification is changing the DNA of an organism.

Cloned Mammals Can be Made by Adult Cell Cloning

Dolly the sheep (born in 1996) was the first mammal cloned from an adult cell. This is how it was done:

1) Dolly was made by taking a sheep's egg cell and removing its nucleus — leaving the cell without any genetic material. The nucleus removed from the egg cell was haploid (only containing half the normal number of chromosomes) because the egg cell was a gamete.

2) Another nucleus was inserted into the egg cell in its place. This was a diploid nucleus from a cell of the parent sheep and it contained the full number of chromosomes.

3) The cell was stimulated so that it started dividing by mitosis, as if it was a normal fertilised egg cell. It formed an embryo.

4) The embryo was implanted into the uterus of a female sheep, which carried it and gave birth to it. The new sheep was genetically identical to the parent sheep which the nucleus was taken from.

Adult cell cloning

Egg — Adult body cell

Nucleus removed — Nucleus removed

Cell is stimulated to divide

Live animal

Cloned Mammals Don't Live As Long

1) Dolly the sheep only lived for 6 years (half as long as many sheep). She was put down because she had lung disease, and she also had arthritis. These diseases are more usual in older sheep. Because Dolly was cloned from an older sheep, it's been suggested her 'true' age may have been older. But it's possible she was just unlucky — and that her illnesses weren't linked to her being a clone.

2) There are many risks and problems associated with cloning:
   • The cloning process often fails. It took hundreds of attempts to clone Dolly.
   • Clones are often born with genetic defects.
   • Cloned animals' immune systems are sometimes unhealthy — so they suffer from more diseases.

Genes Can be Transferred into Animals and Plants

Useful genes can be transferred into the DNA of animals and plants at a very early stage of their development — shortly after fertilisation. This is called genetic modification. It has many potential uses.

1) Genetically modified (GM) plants have been developed that are resistant to viruses and herbicides (chemicals used to kill weeds). And long-life tomatoes can be made by changing the gene that causes the fruit to ripen.

2) Genes can also be inserted into animal embryos so that the animal grows up to have more useful characteristics. For example, sheep have been genetically engineered to produce drugs in their milk that can be used to treat human diseases.

3) Genetic disorders like cystic fibrosis are caused by faulty genes. Scientists are trying to cure these diseases by inserting working genes into sufferers. This is called gene therapy (see p.16).

Genetic modification has the potential for solving many problems, but not everyone thinks it's great.

1) Some people strongly believe that we shouldn't go tinkering about with genes because it's not natural.

2) There are also worries that changing an organism's genes might accidentally create unplanned problems — which could then get passed on to future generations.

Star Wars II: Attack of Dolly the Sheep...

Cloning is still in its early days — at the moment cloned animals often have health problems. In the future, cloning might be really useful for copying animals or plants with good characteristics (e.g. good quality wool). But this would mean even less variety in the gene pool than with selective breeding.

Gene Therapy

And finally, here's a lovely page about gene therapy to wrap up the section.

Inherited Disorders are Caused by Faulty Genes

1) Each gene in your DNA (see p.4) codes for the production of a specific protein.
2) If a gene is faulty, it might produce the wrong protein or not produce a protein at all.
3) This can cause genetic disorders, e.g. cystic fibrosis, haemophilia and sickle-cell anaemia. These disorders are hereditary — parents can pass the gene on to their children.
4) Sometimes a single faulty gene causes a disorder, e.g. cystic fibrosis. Cystic fibrosis is a disorder of the cell membranes, and causes thick mucus to be produced, e.g. in the lungs and digestive system.
5) Other diseases are thought to be caused by a combination of inherited genes and environmental factors, e.g. some types of cancer.

Gene Therapy Could be Used to Treat Genetic Disorders

1) Gene therapy is a new, experimental treatment for genetic disorders.
2) It can involve inserting a new, functional version of a faulty gene into a patient's cells. These cells would then be able to make the correct protein and the symptoms would disappear.
3) The gene therapy would be targeted at areas that were badly affected by the disease.
4) In the long term, scientists hope to make these changes to the patient's DNA permanent, but so far, trials testing gene therapy have only shown very temporary improvements.

There are a few possibilities for treating cancer with gene therapy

- Genetic material could be introduced that improves the body's natural immune response, e.g. it could make the cancer cells more obvious to the cells of the immune system.
- The gene therapy could be targeted at the cancer cells to cause their death or stop them growing. E.g. a gene for a drug could be introduced into the cancer cells which would produce the drug and kill the cell. These are called 'suicide genes'.
- The cancer cells could be targeted with genes that will make them more sensitive to treatments like chemotherapy and radiotherapy.
- If a person carries a version of a gene that makes them more likely to get cancer, a normal copy of the gene could be introduced. This may prevent the cancer from developing in the first place, but couldn't be used to treat an existing disease.

5) Gene therapy still needs a lot of research and testing. Potential dangers of gene therapy have already been found, e.g. the introduced genetic material could insert into the middle of another gene, causing a whole new set of medical problems, or 'suicide genes' could be taken up by healthy cells.

The Faulty Genes Will Still be Passed On Though

1) Even if someone is treated with gene therapy their children will still inherit the faulty gene.
2) This is because gene therapy is targeted to the area of the body the disease affects. The working, healthy gene is only incorporated into those specific cells and not into the reproductive cells that make eggs and sperm. It would be very, very difficult to target the reproductive cells using gene therapy.
3) To eradicate the disease from a family you would need to select a healthy embryo during IVF or genetically engineer the embryo to replace the faulty gene (which is illegal in the UK).

Gene therapy — talk things through with your Levi's...

Gene therapy is another ethical minefield. It throws up all sorts of questions, including exactly what should be classed as a 'disease' that needs fixing. Many people would argue that treating cystic fibrosis is a good thing, but what about high blood pressure, or inability to tan... where does it stop?

Revision Summary for B2 Topic 2

Well done, you've finished another topic. And what an incredibly tricky topic it was — especially all the ins and outs of cloning and gene therapy. Award yourself a gold star, relax, get a cup of tea, and take a leisurely glance through these beautiful revision summary questions. Once you've glanced through them, you'll have to answer them. And then you'll have to check your answers and go back and revise any bits you got wrong. And then do the questions again. In fact, it's not really a matter of relaxing at all. More a matter of knuckling down to lots of hard work. Oops. Sorry.

1) Give three ways that the growth of an organism can be measured.

2) What is continuous variation? Give an example.

3) Give an example of an animal which can regenerate.

4) Why is it illegal for athletes to use growth factors to enhance their performance?

5) What is the Hayflick limit? What two types of cell don't have a Hayflick limit?

6) The table below compares mitosis and meiosis. Complete the table using crosses (X) and ticks (✓) to show whether the statements are true for mitosis or meiosis. The first row's been filled in for you.

	Mitosis	Meiosis
Its purpose is to provide new cells for growth and repair.	✓	X
Its purpose is to create gametes (sex cells).		
The cells produced are genetically identical.		
Four cells are produced.		
The cells produced are diploid.		

7) What is meant by the 'differentiation' of cells?

8) How are the stem cells in an embryo different from the stem cells in an adult?

9) There are concerns about the ethics of stem cell research. Give one argument in favour of stem cell research and one argument against stem cell research.

10) Why is the legal time limit for terminating a foetus set at 24 weeks?

11) Why is the amount of light available an important factor in plant growth?

12) Why do plants need oxygen in order to grow?

13) Name a plant which grows in poor conditions. Explain how it is adapted to surviving in these conditions.

14) Explain how auxins cause plant shoots to grow towards light.

15) Explain how auxins cause plant roots to grow towards water.

16) What is selective breeding?

17) Give three examples of the use of selective breeding in farming.

18) Describe two disadvantages of selective breeding.

19) Describe the process of cloning an animal from an adult cell (e.g. cloning a sheep).

20) Describe three risks associated with trying to clone animals.

21) What is genetic modification?

22) Describe how gene therapy could be used to treat a disease caused by a single gene mutation.

23) Describe three ways that gene therapy might be able to help someone suffering from cancer.

24) If someone with a genetic disease is treated with gene therapy, is it possible that their children will inherit the faulty gene?

B2 Topic 3 — Energy Flow

Plants and Photosynthesis

This topic is about the processes that allow <u>environmental conditions</u> on <u>Earth</u> to stay <u>balanced</u> — and how <u>human actions</u> can sometimes affect these processes.

Plant and Animal Cells Have Similarities and Differences

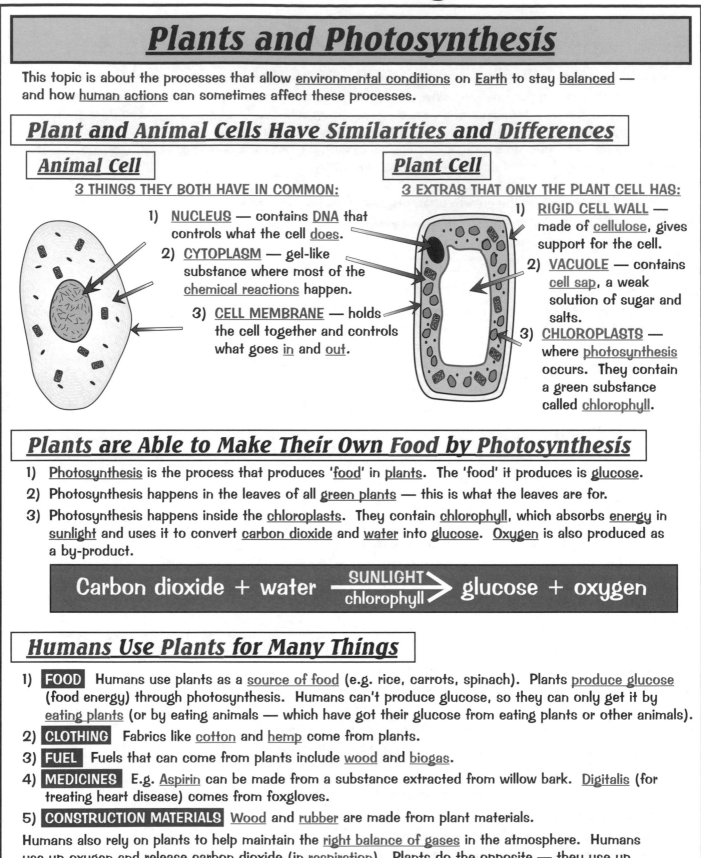

Animal Cell

3 THINGS THEY BOTH HAVE IN COMMON:

1) <u>NUCLEUS</u> — contains <u>DNA</u> that controls what the cell <u>does</u>.

2) <u>CYTOPLASM</u> — gel-like substance where most of the <u>chemical reactions</u> happen.

3) <u>CELL MEMBRANE</u> — holds the cell together and controls what goes <u>in</u> and <u>out</u>.

Plant Cell

3 EXTRAS THAT ONLY THE PLANT CELL HAS:

1) <u>RIGID CELL WALL</u> — made of <u>cellulose</u>, gives support for the cell.

2) <u>VACUOLE</u> — contains <u>cell sap</u>, a weak solution of sugar and salts.

3) <u>CHLOROPLASTS</u> — where <u>photosynthesis</u> occurs. They contain a green substance called <u>chlorophyll</u>.

Plants are Able to Make Their Own Food by Photosynthesis

1) <u>Photosynthesis</u> is the process that produces 'food' in <u>plants</u>. The 'food' it produces is <u>glucose</u>.

2) Photosynthesis happens in the leaves of all <u>green plants</u> — this is what the leaves are for.

3) Photosynthesis happens inside the <u>chloroplasts</u>. They contain <u>chlorophyll</u>, which absorbs <u>energy</u> in <u>sunlight</u> and uses it to convert <u>carbon dioxide</u> and <u>water</u> into <u>glucose</u>. <u>Oxygen</u> is also produced as a by-product.

$$\text{Carbon dioxide} + \text{water} \xrightarrow[\text{chlorophyll}]{\text{SUNLIGHT}} \text{glucose} + \text{oxygen}$$

Humans Use Plants for Many Things

1) **FOOD** Humans use plants as a <u>source of food</u> (e.g. rice, carrots, spinach). Plants <u>produce glucose</u> (food energy) through photosynthesis. Humans can't produce glucose, so they can only get it by <u>eating plants</u> (or by eating animals — which have got their glucose from eating plants or other animals).

2) **CLOTHING** Fabrics like <u>cotton</u> and <u>hemp</u> come from plants.

3) **FUEL** Fuels that can come from plants include <u>wood</u> and <u>biogas</u>.

4) **MEDICINES** E.g. <u>Aspirin</u> can be made from a substance extracted from willow bark. <u>Digitalis</u> (for treating heart disease) comes from foxgloves.

5) **CONSTRUCTION MATERIALS** <u>Wood</u> and <u>rubber</u> are made from plant materials.

Humans also rely on plants to help maintain the <u>right balance of gases</u> in the atmosphere. Humans use up oxygen and release carbon dioxide (in <u>respiration</u>). Plants do the opposite — they use up carbon dioxide and release oxygen (in <u>photosynthesis</u>). These two processes balance each other out, and ensure that the <u>levels of carbon dioxide</u> and <u>oxygen</u> in the atmosphere <u>remain fairly constant</u>.

I'm working on sunshine... woah o....

Plants are pretty crucial in ensuring the <u>flow of energy</u> through nature. They are able to use the Sun's energy to <u>make glucose</u> — the <u>energy source</u> which humans and animals need for <u>respiration</u> (see p.1). Make sure you know the photosynthesis equation inside out — it's important later in the section too.

Rate of Photosynthesis

A plant's rate of photosynthesis is affected by the amount of <u>light</u>, the amount of <u>CO_2</u>, and the <u>temperature</u> of its surroundings. Photosynthesis slows down or stops if the conditions aren't right.

The Limiting Factor Depends on the Conditions

1) A limiting factor is something which <u>stops photosynthesis from happening any faster</u>. The amount of light, CO_2 and the temperature can all be the limiting factor.

2) The limiting factor depends on the <u>environmental conditions</u>. E.g. in <u>winter</u> cold temperatures might be the limiting factor, at <u>night</u> light might be the limiting factor.

There are Three Important Graphs for Rate of Photosynthesis

1) Not Enough LIGHT Slows Down the Rate of Photosynthesis

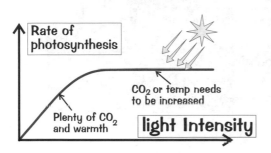

<u>Chlorophyll</u> uses <u>light energy</u> to perform photosynthesis. It can only do it as quickly as the light energy is arriving.

1) If the <u>light level</u> is raised, the rate of photosynthesis will <u>increase steadily</u>, but only up to a <u>certain point</u>.

2) Beyond that, it won't make any <u>difference</u> because then it'll be either the <u>temperature</u> or the <u>CO_2</u> level which is now the limiting factor.

2) Too Little CARBON DIOXIDE Also Slows It Down

<u>CO_2</u> is one of the <u>raw materials</u> needed for photosynthesis — only <u>0.04%</u> of the air is CO_2, so it's <u>pretty scarce</u> as far as plants are concerned.

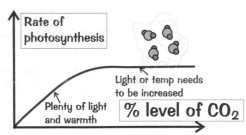

1) As with light intensity, the amount of CO_2 will only <u>increase</u> the rate of photosynthesis up to a point. After this the graph <u>flattens out</u>, showing that CO_2 is no longer the limiting factor.

2) As long as <u>light</u> and <u>CO_2</u> are in plentiful supply then the factor limiting photosynthesis must be <u>temperature</u>.

3) The TEMPERATURE Has to be Just Right

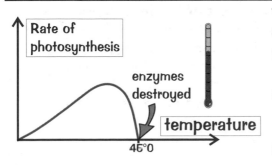

Temperature affects the rate of photosynthesis — because it affects the <u>enzymes</u> involved.

1) As the <u>temperature increases</u>, so does the <u>rate</u> of photosynthesis — up to a point.

2) If the temperature is <u>too high</u> (over about 45 °C), the plant's <u>enzymes</u> will be <u>denatured</u> (destroyed), so the rate of photosynthesis rapidly decreases.

3) <u>Usually</u> though, if the temperature is the <u>limiting factor</u> it's because it's too low, and things need <u>warming up a bit</u>.

No, no... no, no, no, no... no, no, no, no... no, no, there's no limit...

You might get a question on limiting factors in the exam. Don't panic — just <u>use your noggin</u>. Take a <u>good look at the graph</u>. If the rate of photosynthesis goes down when the light level goes down then it's likely that light is the limiting factor. Easy really. The same goes for CO_2 and temperature.

The Carbon Cycle

Carbon flows through the Earth's ecosystems in the <u>carbon cycle</u>. The beauty of the carbon cycle is that carbon is <u>recycled</u> — it's <u>used by organisms</u> but then ends up back in the atmosphere again.

The Carbon Cycle Shows How Carbon is Recycled

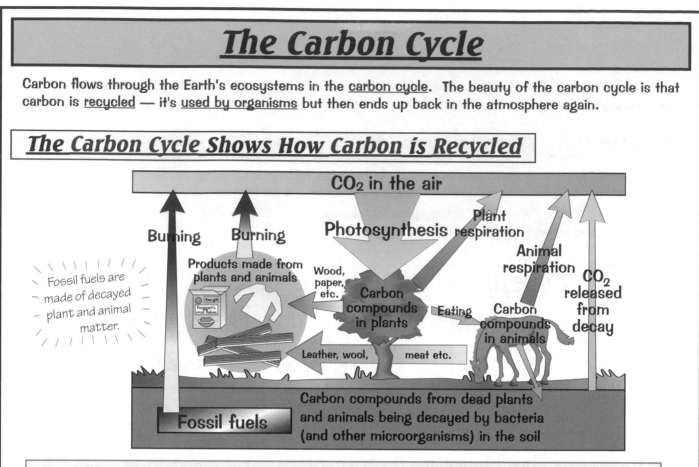

This diagram isn't half as bad as it looks. <u>Learn</u> these important points:

1) There's only <u>one arrow</u> going <u>down</u>. The only thing that <u>removes CO$_2$</u> from the atmosphere is <u>photosynthesis</u> — green plants use it to make carbohydrates, fats and proteins.

2) Both plant and animal <u>respiration</u> put CO$_2$ <u>back into the atmosphere</u>.

3) Dead plants and animals can go <u>three ways</u>: be <u>eaten</u>, be <u>decayed</u> by <u>microorganisms</u> or be turned into <u>useful products</u> by humans.

4) <u>Eating</u> transfers some of the fats, proteins and carbohydrates to <u>new</u> fats, proteins and carbohydrates <u>in the animal</u> doing the eating.

5) Plant and animal products either <u>decay</u> or are <u>burned</u> (combustion) and <u>CO$_2$</u> <u>is released</u>.

Nutrients are Constantly Recycled

1) <u>Living things</u> are made of elements they take from the world around them.

2) It's not just carbon that plants take from the environment. <u>Plants</u> also take elements like <u>oxygen</u>, <u>hydrogen</u> and <u>nitrogen</u> from the <u>soil</u> or the <u>air</u>. They turn these elements into the <u>complex compounds</u> (carbohydrates, proteins and fats) that make up living organisms.

3) These elements are <u>returned</u> to the environment in <u>waste products</u> produced by the organisms, or when the organisms <u>die</u>. Dead organisms decay because they're <u>broken down</u> (digested) by <u>microorganisms</u> — that's how the elements get put back into the <u>soil</u>.

4) All the important <u>elements</u> are <u>recycled</u> — they return to the soil or air, ready to be <u>used</u> by new <u>plants</u> and put back into the <u>food chain</u>.

5) In a <u>stable community</u> the materials <u>taken out</u> of the soil and air are <u>balanced</u> by those that are put <u>back in</u>. There's a constant <u>cycle</u> happening.

What goes around, comes around...

The amount of CO$_2$ produced <u>should balance</u> the amount of CO$_2$ absorbed by plants. <u>But</u> at the moment the level of CO$_2$ is increasing — because we're burning loads of fossil fuels (which produce CO$_2$) and cutting down loads of trees (which then can't absorb any CO$_2$). There's more on this on p.24.

Minerals and Plants

Plants <u>need minerals</u> to live. They have to absorb them from the soil.

Plants Have a Big Surface Area at the Roots to Absorb Minerals

1) Plants have a <u>large root network</u> for absorbing <u>minerals</u> and <u>water</u> from the soil.

2) The cells on plant roots have bits shaped like <u>long</u> '<u>hairs</u>' which stick out into the soil. This gives the roots a <u>large surface area</u> for absorption.

3) Here's what the plant <u>uses</u> some of the minerals for:

Mineral	Function
Nitrate	Needed to make proteins
Phosphate	Needed for photosynthesis and respiration
Magnesium	Needed to make chlorophyll

Root Hairs Take in Minerals Using Active Transport

1) The concentration of <u>minerals</u> is usually <u>higher</u> in the <u>root hair</u> cell than in the <u>soil</u> around it. This means that minerals <u>can't</u> be absorbed into the roots by normal <u>diffusion</u> (see p.1).

2) Instead, plants use a <u>process</u> called <u>active transport</u> to absorb minerals.

3) Active transport <u>pumps</u> minerals from the soil into the root hair cell. Active transport can work <u>against</u> a concentration gradient. It <u>needs energy</u> from <u>respiration</u> to power the pump.

Fertilisers Contain Minerals — But Need to be Used with Care

1) <u>Fertilisers</u> which contain <u>nitrates</u> are essential to <u>modern farming</u>. Without them crops wouldn't grow nearly so well, and <u>food yields</u> would be <u>well down</u>. This is because the crops take <u>nitrates</u> out of the soil and these nitrates need to be <u>replaced</u>.

2) The <u>problems</u> start if some of the <u>rich fertiliser</u> finds its way into <u>rivers</u> and <u>streams</u>.

3) This happens quite easily if <u>too much fertiliser</u> is applied, especially if it rains soon afterwards.

4) The result is <u>eutrophication</u>. As the picture shows, <u>too many nitrates</u> in the water cause a sequence of '<u>mega-growth</u>', '<u>mega-death</u>' and '<u>mega-decay</u>' involving most of the <u>plant</u> and <u>animal life</u> in the water. (<u>Raw sewage</u> pumped into rivers also causes eutrophication.)

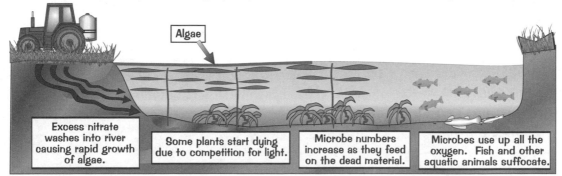

Algae

| Excess nitrate washes into river causing rapid growth of algae. | Some plants start dying due to competition for light. | Microbe numbers increase as they feed on the dead material. | Microbes use up all the oxygen. Fish and other aquatic animals suffocate. |

5) <u>Farmers</u> need to take <u>a lot of care</u> when spreading <u>artificial fertilisers</u> to make sure they avoid causing this kind of <u>environmental damage</u>. (Natural fertilisers, like <u>manure</u>, are <u>less likely</u> to cause eutrophication because they're less soluble.)

Essential to plants, and essential to your biology revision...

<u>Minerals</u> are essential to <u>plant growth</u> — so more minerals means more growth. Farmers take advantage of this by adding fertilisers which can increase their crop yields. But they need to be careful, because if they change the natural environment too much it can cause <u>damage to plants and wildlife</u>.

The Nitrogen Cycle

The <u>flow of nitrates</u> through the atmosphere, soil and living organisms is called the <u>nitrogen cycle</u>. It's similar to the carbon cycle (p.20) — but a tad more complicated...

The Nitrogen Cycle is the Flow of Nitrogen Through Nature

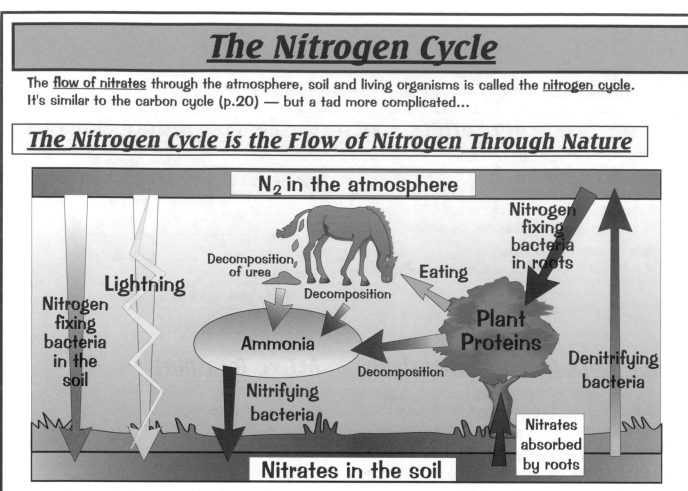

1) The <u>atmosphere</u> contains <u>78% nitrogen gas</u>, N_2. This is <u>very unreactive</u> and so it can't be used <u>directly</u> by plants or animals.

2) <u>Nitrogen</u> is <u>needed</u> for making <u>proteins</u> for growth, so living organisms have to get it somehow.

3) Plants get their nitrogen from the <u>soil</u>, so nitrogen in the air has to be turned into <u>nitrogen compounds</u> before plants can use it. <u>Animals</u> can only get <u>proteins</u> by eating plants (or each other).

4) <u>Decomposers</u> break down <u>proteins</u> in rotting plants and animals, and <u>urea</u> in animal waste, into <u>ammonia</u>. So the nitrogen in these organisms is <u>recycled</u>.

5) <u>Nitrogen fixation</u> isn't an obsession with nitrogen — it's the process of turning <u>N_2 from the air</u> into <u>nitrogen compounds</u> in the soil which <u>plants can use</u>. There are <u>two main ways</u> that this happens:
   a) <u>Lightning</u> — there's so much <u>energy</u> in a bolt of lightning that it's enough to make nitrogen <u>react with oxygen</u> in the air to give nitrates.
   b) <u>Nitrogen-fixing bacteria</u> in roots and soil (see below).

6) There are <u>four</u> different types of <u>bacteria</u> involved in the nitrogen cycle:

   a) <u>DECOMPOSERS</u> — decompose <u>proteins</u> and <u>urea</u> and turn them into <u>ammonia</u>.
   b) <u>NITRIFYING BACTERIA</u> — turn <u>ammonia</u> in decaying matter into <u>nitrates</u>.
   c) <u>NITROGEN-FIXING BACTERIA</u> — turn <u>atmospheric N_2</u> into <u>nitrogen compounds</u> that plants can use.
   d) <u>DENITRIFYING BACTERIA</u> — turn <u>nitrates</u> back into <u>N_2 gas</u>. This is of no benefit to living organisms.

7) Some <u>nitrogen-fixing bacteria</u> live in the <u>soil</u>. Others live in <u>nodules</u> on the roots of <u>legume plants</u> (e.g. peas and beans). This is why legume plants are so good at putting nitrogen <u>back into the soil</u>. The plants have a <u>mutualistic relationship</u> with the bacteria — the bacteria get <u>food</u> (sugars) from the plant, and the plant gets <u>nitrogen compounds</u> from the bacteria to make into <u>proteins</u>.

I wish I had some information-fixing bacteria...

The nitrogen cycle is probably the <u>scariest looking diagram</u> you'll see in the whole of GCSE Additional Science. But learn it you must. The horse being in the sky is just a bit of artistic licence...

Life on Mars

Don't get too excited, this page isn't about little green men... it's about whether we could live on <u>Mars</u>.

A Biosphere is a Closed Environment

The Earth is one big ecosystem called a <u>biosphere</u>. The Earth's biosphere includes <u>all the living things</u> on Earth, plus the <u>environment</u> in which they live. Recently, scientists have tried to create <u>artificial biospheres</u> — <u>sealed, self-contained environments</u>, e.g. <u>Biosphere 2</u> in America.

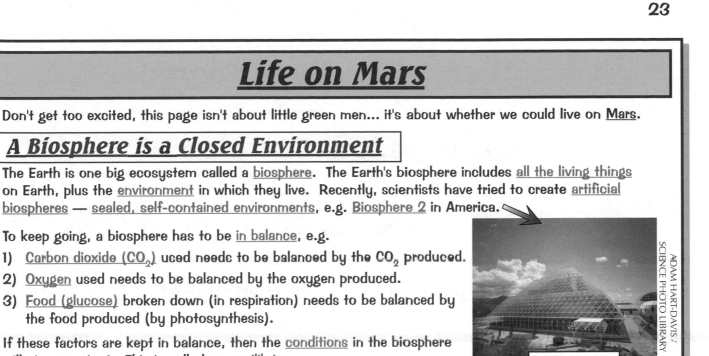

ADAM HART-DAVIS /
SCIENCE PHOTO LIBRARY

Biosphere 2

To keep going, a biosphere has to be <u>in balance</u>, e.g.

1) <u>Carbon dioxide (CO$_2$)</u> used needs to be balanced by the CO$_2$ produced.

2) <u>Oxygen</u> used needs to be balanced by the oxygen produced.

3) <u>Food (glucose)</u> broken down (in respiration) needs to be balanced by the food produced (by photosynthesis).

If these factors are kept in balance, then the <u>conditions</u> in the biosphere will <u>stay constant</u>. This is called an <u>equilibrium</u>.

Living things <u>depend on each other</u> to keep this <u>equilibrium</u> in the <u>biosphere</u>, e.g.

1) Plants make <u>food (glucose)</u> by photosynthesis (see p.18). This is <u>used by animals</u>, including humans, who can't produce glucose themselves.

2) Microorganisms <u>break down dead matter</u> into simple substances (e.g. carbon dioxide and nitrates) that plants can use.

3) Plants <u>use up carbon dioxide</u> and <u>produce oxygen</u> in photosynthesis. Animals, plants and microorganisms <u>use up oxygen</u> and <u>produce carbon dioxide</u> in respiration.

A Biosphere Could be Used to Colonise Mars

1) The planet <u>Mars</u> has a <u>very different environment</u> from Earth — it wouldn't be possible for organisms from Earth to survive in Mars' natural environment. For example, the Earth's atmosphere contains about 21% oxygen, but Mars' atmosphere only contains about 0.15%.

2) It has been suggested that one way humans could survive on Mars is if they <u>set up an artificial biosphere</u> there. The artificial biosphere would be a <u>self-contained</u>, <u>sealed environment</u> containing similar conditions to Earth. It would be <u>similar</u> to the artificial biospheres which scientists have set up on Earth, like <u>Biosphere 2</u>.

3) Biosphere 2 was set up as a huge, sealed ecosystem in Arizona in the USA in the 1990s. Scientists managed to <u>live inside it</u> for two years, <u>using plants</u> to grow their food, and <u>recycling their waste and nutrients</u>. Another project is going on now, in an artificial biosphere in the <u>Arctic</u> called <u>Mars on Earth</u>. If it is successful, it's possible that scientists will try something similar in space...

There are a Few Problems Though

So far, no human has travelled to Mars. Even if humans managed to reach Mars, setting up a biosphere there <u>wouldn't be easy</u>. The <u>temperature</u> on Mars is an average of –63 °C, so the biosphere would need to be <u>kept warm</u>, possibly with fuel from plants grown in the biosphere. Also the atmosphere on Mars is very high in CO$_2$ and low in O$_2$ — you'd need to create a <u>different atmosphere</u> inside the biosphere if humans were to survive there. There's also the fairly major challenge of <u>transporting</u> all the equipment, construction materials and living organisms to Mars in the first place.

Life on Mars — not just in Bowie's imagination...

Sustaining an artificial biosphere is difficult — even on Earth. After two years of humans living in Biosphere 2, oxygen levels dipped and there were dangerous levels of nitrous oxide. They had <u>failed to keep the equilibrium</u> (balance) right. But maybe in the future <u>new technology</u> will solve the problems.

There's Too Many People

We have an <u>impact</u> on the world around us — and the <u>more humans</u> there are, the bigger the impact.

There're About 6.5 Billion People in the World

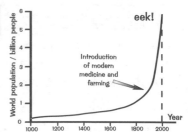

1) The <u>population</u> of the world is currently <u>rising</u> very quickly, and it's not slowing down — look at the graph...

2) This is mostly due to <u>modern medicine</u>, which has <u>reduced</u> the number of people dying from <u>disease</u>. <u>Modern farming methods</u> enable greater levels of food production.

...with Increasing Demands on the Environment

When the <u>Earth's population</u> was much smaller, the effects of <u>human activity</u> were usually <u>small</u> and <u>local</u>. Nowadays though, our actions can have a far more <u>widespread</u> effect.

1) Our rapidly increasing <u>population</u> puts pressure on the <u>environment</u>, as we <u>take the resources</u> we need to <u>survive</u>.

2) The <u>increasing standard of living</u> in all countries also has an impact on the environment — more people own products like cars, televisions, washing machines, refrigerators... It means we use more <u>raw materials</u>, more <u>energy</u> for the <u>manufacturing processes</u> and more energy to <u>power these products</u>.

3) Unfortunately, many raw materials are being used up quicker than they're being replaced. If we carry on like we are, one day they're going to <u>run out</u>. Our use of resources is <u>unsustainable</u>.

4) The growth in population and living standards also results in <u>more waste</u>. Unless this waste is properly handled, more <u>harmful pollution</u> will be caused.

Deforestation Increases Carbon Dioxide Levels

People around the world are <u>cutting down</u> large areas of forest (<u>deforestation</u>) for <u>timber</u> and to clear land for <u>farming</u>. This increases the <u>level of carbon dioxide</u> in the <u>atmosphere</u> because:

- Carbon dioxide is <u>released</u> when trees are <u>burnt</u> to clear land. (Carbon in wood is 'locked up' and doesn't contribute to atmospheric CO_2 — until it's released by burning.)
- <u>Microorganisms</u> feeding on bits of <u>dead wood</u> release CO_2 as a waste product of <u>respiration</u>.
- Because living trees use CO_2 for <u>photosynthesis</u>, removing these trees means <u>less</u> CO_2 is removed from the atmosphere.

So more CO_2 is being put into the atmosphere and less is being taken out.

Carbon Dioxide is a Greenhouse Gas

1) The <u>temperature</u> of the Earth is a <u>balance</u> between the heat it gets from the Sun and the heat it radiates back out into space.

2) Gases in the <u>atmosphere</u> like <u>carbon dioxide</u> and <u>methane</u> naturally act like an <u>insulating layer</u>. They are often called 'greenhouse gases'. They absorb most of the heat that would normally be radiated out into space, and re-radiate it in all directions — including back towards the Earth.

3) <u>Human activity</u> affects the <u>amount of greenhouse gases</u> in the atmosphere, e.g. CO_2 from deforestation.

4) There's evidence that the Earth is <u>warming up</u>, which <u>might</u> be linked to increasing levels of greenhouse gases. This is called <u>global warming</u> and it may cause <u>climate change</u>.

More people, more resources used, more waste, fewer trees...

It's a <u>sticky problem</u>. On the one hand, it's great that we have <u>nicer lifestyles</u> and <u>better medicine</u> than they did in the Middle Ages. But it's possible that we're paying for it with environmental damage...

Climate Change and Food Distribution

Most climate scientists agree that the Earth is getting warmer. They're now trying to work out what the effects of global warming might be — sadly, it's not as simple as everyone having nicer summers.

The Consequences of Global Warming Could be Pretty Serious

If climate scientists are right, there are several reasons to be worried about global warming. Here's a few:

1) As the sea gets warmer, it expands, causing sea levels to rise. This would be bad news for people living in low-lying places, like the Netherlands, East Anglia and the Maldives — they could be flooded.

2) Hurricanes form over water that's warmer than 26 °C — so if there's more warm water, you would expect more hurricanes.

3) Higher temperatures make ice melt. Water that's currently 'trapped' on land (as ice) will run into the sea, causing sea levels to rise even more. Lots of new water entering the sea could also disrupt ocean currents.

4) As weather patterns change, the food we grow will be affected, all over the world. Droughts in some places could force millions of people to move.

> You'll notice that the word 'could' pops up quite a bit. That's because the climate is such a complicated system. For instance, if the ice melts, there's less white stuff around to reflect the Sun's rays out to space, so maybe we'll absorb more heat and get even warmer. But... when the sea's warmer, more water evaporates, making more clouds — and they reflect the Sun's rays, so maybe we'd cool down again. So it's hard to predict exactly what will happen, but lots of people are working on it, and it's not looking too good.

Scientists have come up with computer programs to try and predict the consequences of climate change. Some predict a 'white world' — the whole world covered in ice. Others predict a very hot climate.

Not Everyone Has Enough Food to Eat

1) According to the United Nations World Food Programme, in 2000-2002 there were 852 million undernourished people worldwide. Of these, 815 million lived in developing countries.

2) Total world food production is enough to feed the Earth's population, but despite this millions of people are short of food. This is because food is not equally distributed. Some countries have a food surplus, while others have a food shortage.

3) Reasons for food shortages include: climates or soils which are not suitable for agriculture, pests like locusts which destroy crops, natural disasters like floods and droughts, and wars which often force people to leave their homes and land. Some reasons for food shortages are connected to poverty, e.g. farmers in developing countries may not have the funds to invest in new agricultural technology or access to education in efficient farming methods.

4) Some industrialised countries (for example in the EU) subsidise their farmers. This protects jobs and food production within the country by enabling farmers to compete with cheap imports from abroad. A disadvantage is that it can lead to overproduction of food in these countries, resulting in surpluses.

5) It can be argued that ethically countries with food surpluses should give food to countries with food shortages, or sell them food at a lower price. But on the other hand it can be argued that giving food away would cause prices to crash and unbalance the world economy. Transportation of food from one area to another can also be a problem — especially if the food shortage is in a dangerous war zone.

It's a threat to the Earth as we know it...

The possible consequences of global warming are pretty scary. Maybe colonising Mars isn't such a crazy idea. You can find out more information about global warming on the Internet. Have a look at websites like www.defra.gov.uk, www.newscientist.com and www.unep.org.

Food Production

There are four main ways to maximise food production: 1) <u>increase the energy transfer</u>, 2) <u>reduce disease</u>, 3) improve <u>feeding/growing conditions</u>, 4) <u>control predators</u>. Learn them.

Understanding Energy Flow Helps to Improve Food Production

1) Energy from the <u>Sun</u> is the source of energy for nearly <u>all</u> life on Earth.

2) <u>Plants</u> use a small percentage of the light energy from the Sun to make <u>glucose</u> during photosynthesis. This energy then works its way through the <u>food chain</u> as animals eat the plants and each other.

3) At each stage in the food chain, some of the <u>energy is used up</u> in respiration.

4) Understanding this is important for <u>efficient food production</u>:

- If you <u>reduce</u> the number of <u>stages in the food chain</u>, you reduce the amount of energy lost. For a given area of land, you can produce <u>more food</u> for humans by growing <u>crops</u> than by grazing <u>animals</u>.
- Food production can also be made more efficient by <u>reducing the amount of energy</u> animals use, e.g. if you keep animals warm and still, they won't use as much energy and won't need to eat as much.

Fish Farms Reduce Energy Loss, Disease and Predators

Fish is an increasingly popular dish, but fish stocks are dwindling. 'Fish farms' were set up to rear fish in a controlled way and increase their production. <u>Salmon farming</u> in Scotland is a good example:

1) The fish are kept in <u>cages</u> in a <u>sea loch</u>, to <u>stop them using energy</u> swimming about looking for food — i.e. they are kept still to maximise the <u>energy transfer</u>.

2) The cage also <u>protects</u> them from <u>predators</u> like birds and seals.

3) They're fed a <u>diet</u> of food pellets that's <u>carefully controlled</u> to <u>maximise</u> energy transfer and to avoid <u>pollution</u> to the loch. (Excess food and poo from the salmon can cause lots of <u>bacteria to grow</u>, which use up <u>oxygen</u> needed by other organisms in the water.)

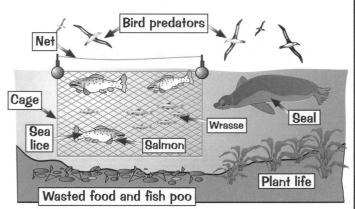

4) Young fish are reared in <u>special tanks</u> to ensure as many survive as possible.

5) Fish kept in cages are more prone to <u>disease</u> and <u>parasites</u>. One pest is <u>sea lice</u>, which can be treated with a <u>chemical pesticide</u> which kills them. To <u>avoid pollution</u> from chemical pesticides, <u>biological pest control</u> can be used instead, e.g. a small fish called a <u>wrasse</u> which eats fish lice off the backs of the salmon, keeping the stock <u>lice-free</u>.

Greenhouses Do the Same Thing

<u>Greenhouses</u> are used to <u>commercially grow plants</u>. The growing conditions can be completely <u>controlled</u>.

1) They <u>trap the Sun's warmth</u>, making the plants grow <u>faster</u> than outside.

2) <u>Carbon dioxide</u> and <u>light</u> levels can be <u>increased</u> to provide <u>optimum conditions</u> for <u>photosynthesis</u> (see p.18) and thereby <u>maximise growth</u>.

3) In greenhouses, plants can be grown <u>out of season</u> using <u>heaters</u> and <u>artificial light</u>.

4) Plants can be kept <u>free from diseases</u> and <u>pests</u> by good <u>hygiene</u> and <u>pest screens</u>. Pests can be <u>controlled</u> with <u>chemicals</u> or <u>biological controls</u>.

Two fish in a tank...

...one says to the other, "How do you drive this thing?" Ahem, sorry. As well as all this stuff on food production, you need to cast your mind back to the energy and biomass info in <u>GCSE Science (B1a Topic 1)</u>. Make sure you can draw pyramids of biomass, and tell your producers from your carnivores...

Revision Summary for B2 Topic 3

This section makes links between topics which at first might seem to have nothing to do with one another. Photosynthesis links to the carbon cycle, which links to deforestation, which links to climate change... And population links to food shortages, which links to efficient food production, which links to fertilisers... If you can get the hang of it, you're a pretty smart cookie. Make sure you've learnt it all by doing these questions. And then doing them again. And then maybe one more time, just for good luck.

1) Name three things which plant and animal cells have in common.

2) Write the word equation for photosynthesis.

3) Give five ways that humans use plants.

4)* The graph shows how the rate of plant growth is affected by increasing the level of carbon dioxide. Look at the graph and answer the two questions below.

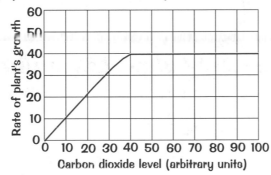

a) At what level of carbon dioxide is the plant's growth limited by another factor?

b) Suggest two possible limiting factors on the plant's growth above this level.

5) What happens to plant enzymes if the temperature is raised over about 45 °C?

6) Sketch the carbon cycle.

7) Give two ways in which the elements an animal eats can be returned to the environment.

8) What is the purpose of a plant's root network?

9) Explain how the shape of root hair cells makes them good at absorption.

10) Why can't plants use diffusion to absorb minerals from the soil? What do they use instead?

11) Explain what eutrophication is.

12) Why is nitrogen needed by plants and animals?

13) What do decomposers do?

14) Sketch out the nitrogen cycle.

15) Give three examples of how living things in a biosphere are dependent on each other.

16) Suggest three reasons why setting up an artificial biosphere on Mars would be tricky.

17) Give two reasons why the world's population is increasing rapidly.

18) Why do increasing standards of living have an impact on the environment?

19) Describe three ways in which deforestation increases the amount of carbon dioxide released into the environment.

20) What are 'greenhouse gases'?

21) Why is it difficult to predict climate change?

22) Give four reasons why an area might have a food shortage.

23) Why might countries with food surpluses not want to give free food to countries with food shortages?

24) Give the four main ways in which it is possible to maximise food production.

25) How can an understanding of energy transfer help to make food production more efficient?

26) Explain how fish farms reduce the following: a) energy loss, b) disease, c) threat of predators.

* Answer on page 37

Population Sizes

Within an ecosystem, different species <u>depend on each other</u> for <u>survival</u>. This is called <u>interdependence</u>.

Adaptation, Competition and Predation Affect Population Size

The <u>size</u> and <u>distribution</u> of the <u>population</u> of a <u>species</u> in an <u>environment</u> depends on three factors:

1) **Adaptation** — how well the species is <u>adapted</u> to the <u>environment</u>.
2) **Competition** — how well the species <u>competes</u> with others for the same <u>resources</u>.
3) **Predation** — how well the species <u>avoids</u> being eaten by <u>predators</u>.

In some species, individuals (or mating pairs) set up <u>territories</u> — an area where they are the only member of that species. Animals <u>mark</u> their territory and <u>defend</u> it. The territory is important — e.g. an area to find <u>food</u>, have a <u>nest</u> and to <u>attract a mate</u>. If each individual or mating pair has its own territory, it <u>reduces competition</u> between members of the <u>same species</u> for the <u>resources</u> in each area.

The Organisms in an Environment Affect Each Other

This is a <u>food web</u> showing how different organisms in a <u>pond</u> depend on each other as a <u>food source</u>.

1) <u>Plants</u> (producers) are at the bottom of the food web — they convert the Sun's energy into <u>glucose</u> by <u>photosynthesis</u>.

2) The water-fleas, snails and larvae <u>eat the plants</u> and are then eaten themselves by <u>predators</u> like fish and leeches.

3) Each animal is <u>dependent</u> on the <u>species it eats</u> for food, e.g. the water snails depend on the large plants for food.

4) Different species may <u>compete</u> for the <u>same food</u>, e.g. the water-fleas and larvae both eat the microscopic plants.

5) At the <u>top</u> of the food web, there is often a <u>large carnivore</u>. In the pond, it might be a large fish like a <u>perch</u>. This animal is usually very <u>well adapted</u> to its <u>environment</u>, e.g. camouflage markings to help it hide, and a strong tail for fast movement to help it catch prey.

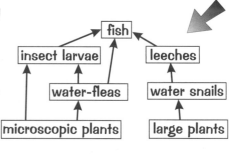

The different species in an environment are <u>interdependent</u>. If <u>one species changes</u>, it <u>affects all the others</u>. For example, if the <u>water-fleas</u> in the pond <u>died</u>, then:

- There would be <u>less food</u> for the <u>fish</u> (a predator of water-fleas), so their numbers <u>might decrease</u>.
- The number of <u>microscopic plants</u> might <u>increase</u>, because the water-fleas wouldn't be eating them.
- The <u>insect larvae</u> would have <u>less competition</u> for food, so their numbers <u>might increase</u>.
- But the effects of change in a food web are <u>unpredictable</u> — e.g. if the fish couldn't eat the water-fleas, they might eat more insect larvae instead — causing the insect larva population to decrease.

Human Activities Affect the Environment

<u>Population size</u> and distribution of organisms can also be <u>affected</u> by <u>human activities</u>. <u>Fishing</u>, <u>pollution</u>, <u>farming</u> and <u>building</u> all affect the <u>environments</u> which organisms live in.

The <u>table</u> shows how the <u>cod population</u> of the North Sea has <u>changed</u>: The two main reasons for the <u>drop</u> in the cod population between 1963 and 2001 were <u>human activities</u> — <u>overfishing</u> and <u>pollution</u>. The <u>population recovery</u> shown by the 2004 figure is mainly due to <u>conservation measures</u>, e.g. limits on how many fish can be caught.

Year	Cod biomass (tonnes)
1963	157 000
2001	38 000
2004	46 000

I'm dependent on Mr Kipling...

In the exam you might be asked to look at <u>data</u> showing how <u>human activity affects environments</u> and population sizes. It might be primary (raw) data or secondary (processed) data. You've been warned.

Extreme Environments

Organisms which live in extreme environments like deserts or deep oceans need to be <u>specially adapted</u>. They <u>avoid competition</u> for resources by living in such strange and dangerous places.

Some Organisms Have Adapted to Living in the Deep Sea

Deep under the surface of the sea, conditions are hard to live in. There's virtually <u>no light</u> (sunlight can't penetrate that deep into the water). That means <u>plants can't grow</u> because they can't photosynthesise. Because there are no plants, <u>food is scarce</u> — organisms survive on scraps that sink down from above.

Some animals have adapted to living in the deep ocean, e.g.

1) Some deep-sea fish are <u>able to emit light</u> from parts of their body. E.g. the angler-fish has a rod-shaped <u>spine</u> sticking out of its face which <u>gives out light</u>. The light <u>attracts prey</u>, which the angler fish then eats.

It is difficult to study deep-sea fish — special sea craft with sensitive underwater cameras are needed.

2) Deep-sea fish often have <u>huge mouths</u>, e.g. the rat-tail fish and viperfish, which move along the seabed scooping up particles of food.

3) Many deep-sea fish have <u>huge eyes</u> adapted to the dark, and <u>long feelers</u> to help them locate prey.

Organisms in Volcanic Vents are Adapted to High Temperatures

There are <u>volcanic vents</u> in the <u>seabed</u> that send out hot water and minerals into the cold ocean. Some organisms have adapted to living around them.

1) The chemicals from the vents support <u>bacteria</u> that are able to make their own <u>food</u> using <u>chemical energy</u>. This is called <u>chemosynthesis</u>. It's a bit like photosynthesis, but (because there's hardly any light down there) it uses chemical energy instead of light energy.

2) These bacteria are at the bottom of a <u>food web</u> — animals feed on the bacteria.

3) The conditions are <u>extremely hot</u> and the bacteria which live near the vents must be specially <u>adapted</u> to cope with the temperature.

Organisms in the Antarctic Have Adapted to the Cold

1) The Antarctic is another extreme environment — it has high winds and a very <u>low average temperature</u> of about −37 °C. The water on land is <u>frozen</u> and there are virtually <u>no plants</u> on the land.

2) The Antarctic <u>food web</u> begins in the ocean. <u>Microscopic marine algae</u> are at the base of the food web. These are eaten by shellfish, which are eaten by many larger animals.

3) Animals such as seals and penguins are <u>adapted</u> to the antarctic environment. E.g. they have lots of <u>fat</u> under the skin (for insulation).

Animals Living at High Altitudes Have Also Adapted

1) Places at <u>high altitude</u> (e.g. up mountains) are also <u>extreme environments</u>.

2) The temperature is <u>cold</u>, especially at night. Atmospheric pressure is low — which means there is <u>less oxygen</u>. There is often a <u>shortage of water</u> — it can drain away or evaporate, or it can freeze.

3) Some <u>animals</u> (like llamas) have adapted to high altitudes. <u>Llamas</u> have a <u>thick fur coat</u> for insulation, and a special type of <u>haemoglobin</u> in their red blood cells to pick up oxygen more easily.

Viperfish — they really are as scary as they sound...

You could go to the most horrible, dry, desolate, smelly, freezing, airless place in the world, and there would still be some <u>well-adapted little critter</u> able to live there. Take my house for example — it's freezing since the boiler broke, but I've adapted (if an extra jumper counts).

Air Pollution — CO_2 and CO

Human activity (e.g. driving around in cars) affects the environment we live in.

The Level of CO_2 in the Atmosphere is Increasing

1) The level of CO_2 in the atmosphere used to be nicely balanced between the CO_2 released by respiration and decomposition (of animals and plants) and the CO_2 absorbed by photosynthesis (see p.18).

2) However, people release carbon dioxide into the atmosphere all the time as part of everyday life — from car exhausts, industrial processes, burning fossil fuels etc. As society has become more industrialised over the last 300 years, the amount of CO_2 released has increased.

3) We have also been cutting down trees all over the world to make space for living and farming. This is called deforestation (see p.24).

4) The level of CO_2 in the atmosphere has gone up by about 20%, and will continue to rise as long as we keep burning fossil fuels — just look at that graph — eek!

5) Many scientists have linked the increasing level of CO_2 with an increase in global temperature ('global warming'), which may be causing climate change.

Carbon Monoxide is Poisonous

1) When fossil fuels are burnt without enough air supply they produce the gas carbon monoxide (CO).

2) It's a poisonous gas. If it combines with red blood cells, it prevents them from carrying oxygen.

3) Carbon monoxide's mostly released in car emissions. Most modern cars are fitted with catalytic converters that oxidise the carbon monoxide (to make carbon dioxide), decreasing the amount that's released into the atmosphere.

You Need to be Able to Interpret Data About CO_2 and CO Pollution

In the exam you might have to interpret data (information) about carbon dioxide and carbon monoxide pollution. Here's an example of some data about carbon monoxide (CO) pollution.

A scientist investigated the level of carbon monoxide (CO) in the air in different locations. Here are the results:

Location	Carbon monoxide concentration (ppm)
Seaside	0.5
City centre	11
City suburbs	4
Near the motorway	9

You could describe the data in this table by saying:

1) The seaside has the lowest CO concentration. The city centre has the highest.

2) The CO concentration in the suburbs is fairly low compared to the city centre and motorway.

3) The CO concentration near the motorway is nearly as high as that in the city centre.

You could then use your knowledge about pollution to interpret the data:

1) CO comes from burning fossil fuels, like coal or petrol.

2) In the city centre and the motorway there are more cars than at the seaside or suburbs. So more fossil fuels are burnt (by the cars), and more CO is produced in these places.

Oh, I do like to be beside the seaside...

The places which organisms live in are often changed by human activity (e.g. pollution of an area by a motorway). This affects the population sizes and distributions of the organisms.

Interpreting Data: Climate Change

The environment <u>doesn't stay the same</u>. One of the things affecting it is <u>climate change</u>.
You have to be able to interpret information about climate change.

Scientists are Monitoring Climate Change

To find out about <u>climate change</u>, scientists are busy collecting <u>data</u> about the environment.

1) They're using <u>satellites</u> to measure the temperature of the <u>sea surface</u> and the amount of snow and ice cover. These are modern, accurate instruments and give us a global coverage.

2) Automatic weather <u>stations</u> tell us the <u>atmospheric temperature</u> at various locations. They contain thermometers that are sensitive and accurate — they can measure to very small fractions of a degree.

You Need to Weigh the Evidence Before Making Judgements

1) All this scientific data is only useful if it covers a <u>wide enough area</u> and a <u>long enough time scale</u>.

2) Generally, observations of a very <u>small area</u> aren't much use by themselves for monitoring global climate change. Noticing that your <u>local glacier</u> seems to be melting does <u>not</u> mean that ice everywhere is melting, and it's certainly <u>not</u> a valid way to show that <u>global temperature</u> is changing. (That would be like going to Wales, seeing a stripy cow and concluding that all the cows in Wales are turning into zebras.) Looking at the area of ice cover over a <u>whole continent</u>, like Antarctica, would be better.

3) The same thing goes for <u>time</u>. It's no good going to the Arctic, seeing four polar bears one week but only two the next week and concluding that polar bears are dying out because the ice is disappearing. You need to do your observations again and again, year after year.

4) Scientists can make mistakes — so don't take one person's word for something, even if they've got a PhD. But if <u>lots</u> of scientists get the <u>same result</u> using different methods, it's much more likely to be right. That's why most governments around the world are starting to take climate change seriously.

Interpreting Data is Tricky

1) This graph shows data for the <u>level of carbon dioxide (CO_2)</u> and the <u>global temperature</u> between 1700 and 2000.

2) It shows temperature and CO_2 both rising very rapidly from about 1850 (as <u>industrialisation</u> increased). Some people argue that this shows CO_2 is <u>responsible</u> for climate change.

3) There have been <u>huge changes</u> in the climate before though (see GCSE Science, Topic 7). And some people argue that the current temperature increase could just be part of this <u>natural variation</u>.

4) But there's a growing consensus among climate scientists that the Earth <u>is warming up</u>, that the warming is <u>more</u> than just natural variation, and that <u>humans</u> are partly <u>causing</u> it by emitting too much CO_2.

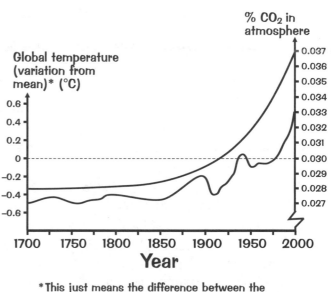

*This just means the difference between the measured <u>temperature</u> and the long-term <u>mean temperature</u> (based on the period 1961 to 1990).

Anthropogenic warming — eh?

There's not too much argument about the 'more CO_2 is making us warmer' theory now (there <u>was</u> plenty of doubt previously, when the data was dodgy). Some people do still question whether the warming is 'anthropogenic' (<u>our fault</u>) or just down to <u>natural variability</u> in the climate. Nothing's ever simple. Sigh.

Air Pollution — Acid Rain

It's not just high levels of carbon dioxide wreaking havoc in the air...

Acid Rain is Caused by Sulphur Dioxide and Oxides of Nitrogen

1) As well as releasing CO_2, burning fossil fuels releases other harmful gases. These include sulphur dioxide and various nitrogen oxides.

2) The sulphur dioxide (SO_2) comes from sulphur impurities in the fossil fuels.

3) The nitrogen oxides are created from a reaction between the nitrogen and oxygen in the air, caused by the heat of the burning. (This can happen in the internal combustion engines of cars.)

4) When these gases mix with rain clouds they form dilute sulphuric acid and dilute nitric acid.

5) This then falls as acid rain.

6) Internal combustion engines in cars and power stations are the main causes of acid rain.

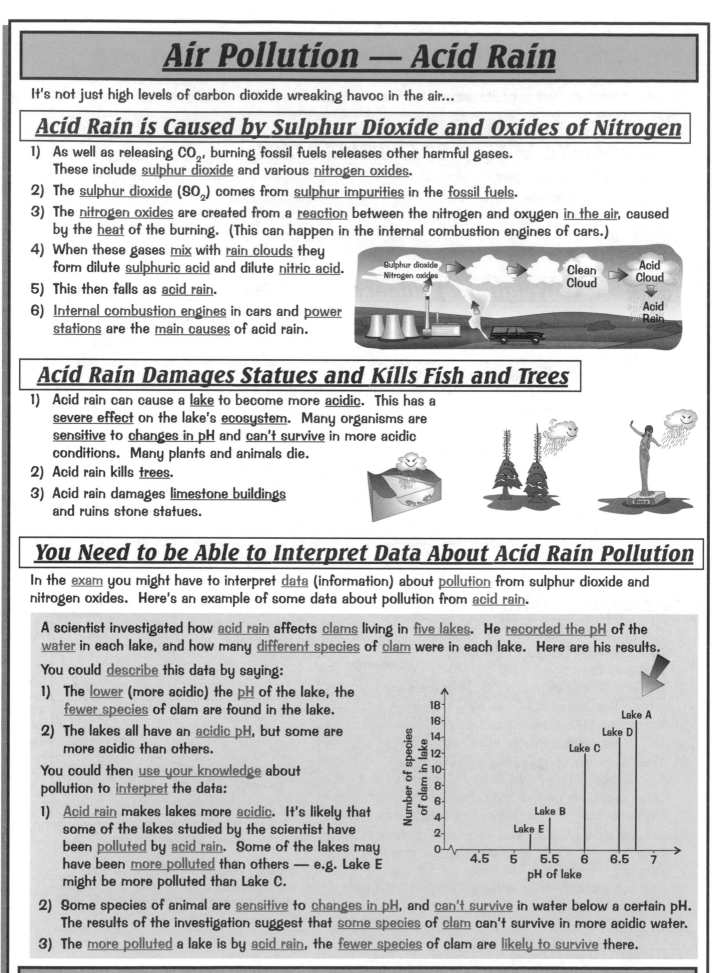

Acid Rain Damages Statues and Kills Fish and Trees

1) Acid rain can cause a lake to become more acidic. This has a severe effect on the lake's ecosystem. Many organisms are sensitive to changes in pH and can't survive in more acidic conditions. Many plants and animals die.

2) Acid rain kills trees.

3) Acid rain damages limestone buildings and ruins stone statues.

You Need to be Able to Interpret Data About Acid Rain Pollution

In the exam you might have to interpret data (information) about pollution from sulphur dioxide and nitrogen oxides. Here's an example of some data about pollution from acid rain.

A scientist investigated how acid rain affects clams living in five lakes. He recorded the pH of the water in each lake, and how many different species of clam were in each lake. Here are his results.

You could describe this data by saying:

1) The lower (more acidic) the pH of the lake, the fewer species of clam are found in the lake.

2) The lakes all have an acidic pH, but some are more acidic than others.

You could then use your knowledge about pollution to interpret the data:

1) Acid rain makes lakes more acidic. It's likely that some of the lakes studied by the scientist have been polluted by acid rain. Some of the lakes may have been more polluted than others — e.g. Lake E might be more polluted than Lake C.

2) Some species of animal are sensitive to changes in pH, and can't survive in water below a certain pH. The results of the investigation suggest that some species of clam can't survive in more acidic water.

3) The more polluted a lake is by acid rain, the fewer species of clam are likely to survive there.

It's raining, it's pouring — quick, cover the rhododendron...

Exam questions about this topic will often give you a graph or table of data to interpret.

Water Pollution

All living things need water. You need water to survive. So it's important it doesn't become polluted...

Many Different Substances Can Pollute Water

1) Fertilisers and Sewage

Fertilisers and sewage are high in nutrients like nitrates and phosphates. Fertilisers used in agriculture sometimes run off into rivers and streams. Treated sewage is released into rivers or the sea (sewage is treated to reduce the amount of nutrients it contains — but it still contains more than clean water). Pollution of water by fertilisers and sewage causes eutrophication (see p.21).

Fertilisers and sewage enter water, adding extra nutrients (phosphates and nitrates).	Algae grow fast.	Algae become overcrowded and start to die.	Bacteria that feed on dead algae use up all the oxygen in the water	Organisms that need oxygen die, e.g. fish.

2) Industrial Chemicals and Pesticides

Chemicals which can cause water pollution include pesticides like DDT (which is now banned in the UK) and industrial chemicals like PCBs. If water is polluted by these, they are taken up by organisms at the bottom of the food chain. Many of these chemicals aren't broken down by the organisms, so when they're eaten the chemical is passed on. The concentration of the chemical increases as it is transferred up the food chain — because each organism eats many of the organisms below it. Organisms near the top of the food chain (e.g. large fish like perch) can accumulate a huge dose and may die.

3) Oil

Spills from oil tanker accidents and also oil from boat engines harm water life.

4) Metals

Some metals (e.g. lead and mercury) are poisonous. They can get into the water supply from old lead pipes or careless waste disposal.

Acid rain (see previous page) is another source of water pollution.

Water Pollution Can be Measured Directly and Indirectly

1) A direct measurement of water pollution is made by taking a sample of water and doing a chemical test to find the concentration of pollutants in it. E.g.
   - The concentration of nitrates, phosphates and pesticides.
   - Oxygen (O_2) concentration (eutrophication would make the O_2 concentration lower).
   - The pH of the water (acid rain reduces the pH).

2) An indirect measurement of water pollution is made by observing the organisms which live in the habitat.
   - Some species (like mayfly larvae) only live in clean water — their presence means pollution is low.
   - Some species (like the rat-tailed maggot) are more common in polluted water.
   - In general, polluted water will contain fewer organisms, and fewer different species.

Here's an example of data about water pollution. The graph shows measurements of nitrates and O_2 concentration at different points along a river.

- The nitrate content of the water increases when sewage enters the river — from the sewage.
- The oxygen concentration falls when sewage enters the river — bacteria breaking down the sewage use up lots of oxygen in respiration.

Polluted water is bad news...

Something needs to be done with waste — and one easy (but flawed) solution is to dump it in the sea.

Living Indicators

Getting an accurate picture of the human impact on the environment is hard.
But there are some <u>useful indicators</u> of how polluted an area is.

Lichen Distribution Indicates the Amount of Air Pollution

1) Some organisms are <u>very sensitive</u> to changes in their environment. These organisms can be used by scientists as an <u>indicator</u> of human impact on the environment (e.g. pollution).

2) For example, <u>air pollution</u> can be monitored by looking at the number and type of <u>lichen</u>, which are very sensitive to levels of <u>sulphur dioxide</u> (and other pollutants) in the atmosphere. This means they can give a good idea about the level of pollution from <u>car exhausts</u>, power stations, etc. The number and type of lichen at a particular location will indicate <u>how clean</u> the air is (e.g. the air is clean if there's <u>lots of lichen</u>).

3) Organisms like lichen are called '<u>indicator species</u>' or '<u>living indicators</u>'.

Here's some <u>data</u> showing the number of <u>different lichen species</u> at <u>five sites</u> in or around London. At <u>each site</u>, scientists examined all the lichens on <u>five randomly selected ash trees</u>.

- The <u>data</u> shows a <u>pattern</u> — there are more lichen species further away from the city centre.

- This is probably because outside the city centre, there is <u>less pollution</u> and the air contains <u>less sulphur dioxide</u> and other pollutants.

Site number	Distance from the city centre (km)	Number of lichen species found on 5 ash trees
1	3	18
2	4	19
3	6	21
4	16	32
5	17	35

Skin Cancer is an Indicator of Ozone Layer Depletion

Another <u>indicator of pollution</u> (and one which affects humans directly) is the number of <u>cases of skin cancer</u>. This has increased in the UK in recent years.

1) It's thought that <u>one reason</u> for the <u>increase in skin cancer</u> is the <u>depletion</u> (thinning) of the <u>ozone layer</u> in the Earth's atmosphere.

2) The ozone layer has got <u>thinner</u> because of <u>air pollution</u> by <u>CFCs</u> (gases which can be used in aerosols, air conditioning and refrigerator coolants). CFCs react with ozone molecules and destroy them.

3) Ozone <u>absorbs</u> harmful <u>ultraviolet (UV) radiation</u> from the Sun. The damage to the ozone layer means it <u>absorbs less UV radiation</u> from the Sun. UV radiation can <u>trigger skin cancer</u> in humans.

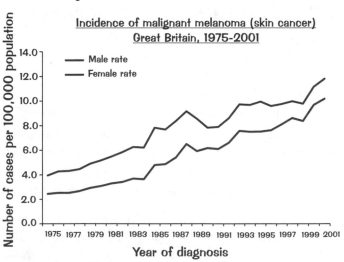

Incidence of malignant melanoma (skin cancer) Great Britain, 1975-2001

— Male rate
— Female rate

Number of cases per 100,000 population

Year of diagnosis

4) Now that the <u>dangers</u> of <u>CFCs</u> are known, they have been <u>banned in many countries</u>. The ozone layer is <u>starting to recover</u>, but this will take time. At the moment, the incidence of skin cancer remains high.

5) By the way, the incidence of skin cancer isn't the only way that scientists can monitor the state of the ozone layer — they can <u>measure it directly</u> with <u>satellites</u> and <u>ground stations</u> too.

My indicators were faulty — I had to keep going left...

Lichen and skin cancer are <u>living indicators</u> showing the effect of pollution. The impact of human activity on the environment can also be monitored by looking at <u>non-living indicators</u>. For example, temperature measurements are a non-living indicator of global warming.

Conservation

Conservation is about <u>protecting</u> the <u>natural environment</u> and its <u>wildlife</u>. Conservation is a way for us to balance out some of the damage we do to the environment (e.g. pollution).

Conservation is Important for Protecting Food, Nature and Culture

1) Conservation measures <u>protect species</u> by <u>maintaining</u> their <u>habitats</u> and <u>protecting</u> them from <u>poachers</u> and <u>over-hunting</u> / <u>over-harvesting</u>.

2) There are several <u>reasons</u> why it's important to <u>conserve species and natural habitats</u>:

- **Protecting endangered species** — Many species are becoming <u>endangered</u>, due to hunting and the <u>destruction</u> of their <u>habitats</u>. They need to be protected to stop them becoming extinct.
- **Protecting the human food supply** — Overfishing has greatly <u>reduced fish stocks</u> in the <u>sea</u>. Conservation measures (e.g. <u>quotas</u> on how many fish can be caught) encourage the survival and <u>growth</u> of fish stocks. This <u>protects the food supply</u> for future generations.
- **Maintaining biodiversity** — <u>Biodiversity</u> is the <u>variety</u> of different <u>species</u> in a habitat — the more species there are, the greater the biodiversity. If one species in a habitat is destroyed it <u>affects</u> the <u>other species</u> living there — the <u>food web</u> will be affected. It's important to protect biodiversity.
- **Cultural heritage** — Some species are important to an area's <u>culture</u> and sense of <u>identity</u>. E.g. the <u>bald eagle</u> is being conserved in the USA as it is regarded as a <u>national symbol</u>.

Conservation Can Lead to Greater Biodiversity

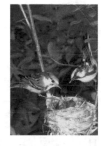

1) Conservation work can help <u>increase</u> the <u>biodiversity</u> (variety of species) in a <u>habitat</u>.

2) <u>Species</u> which have been destroyed or have died out in a habitat can be <u>reintroduced</u>, e.g. if the trees in a habitat have been cut down for timber, new trees can be planted.

3) As biodiversity increases, <u>other species</u> can also be <u>sustained</u> by the habitat (e.g. if trees are planted, then birds might nest in the trees). So the <u>biodiversity</u> of the habitat <u>increases further</u>.

Woodland Conservation Includes Coppicing and Reforestation

A good example of <u>conservation management</u> is in <u>woodland habitats</u>. Conservation organisations like the Woodland Trust help make sure woodland habitats are protected.

Conservation measures in a woodland habitat include:

1) **Coppicing** — This is an ancient form of woodland management. It involves <u>cutting trees</u> down to just above ground level. The <u>stumps</u> sprout <u>straight, new stems</u> which can be regularly harvested.

2) **Reforestation** — Where forests have been cut down in the past, they can be <u>replanted</u>, to <u>recreate</u> the <u>habitat</u> that has been lost.

3) **Replacement planting** — This is when <u>new trees</u> are <u>planted</u> at the <u>same rate</u> that others are <u>cut down</u>. So the total number of trees remains the same.

A coppiced wood in Norfolk

DR JEREMY BURGESS / SCIENCE PHOTO LIBRARY

Save the world — be a tree surgeon...

The organisms in a habitat are dependent on each other — e.g. for food, shelter and nesting sites. You need to <u>protect all the species</u> — animals, trees, fungi, bacteria... because if one of them dies out it affects the others. And that's the story of why this section is called 'interdependence'.

Recycling

Recycling is another good thing that humans can do to <u>reduce our impact</u> on the environment. It means <u>reusing resources</u>, rather than using them once and chucking them in a waste dump.

Recycling Conserves Our Natural Resources

If materials aren't recycled they get <u>thrown away as waste</u>. This means that:

1) There is <u>more waste</u>, so <u>more land</u> has to be used for <u>landfill sites</u> (waste dumps). Some waste is <u>toxic</u> (poisonous), so this also means more polluted land.

2) <u>More materials</u> have to be <u>manufactured</u> or <u>extracted</u> to make new products (rather than recycling existing ones) — using up more of the Earth's resources and more energy.

Recycling uses up less of the Earth's <u>natural resources</u>. <u>Recycling processes</u> usually use <u>less energy</u> and create <u>less pollution</u> than manufacturing or extracting materials from scratch. Recyclable materials include:

1) **Metals** Metals are <u>extracted</u> from <u>ores</u> (e.g. aluminium is extracted from bauxite). There's a <u>limited amount</u> of metal ore — by recycling we make the most of what we've got. Mining and extracting metals takes lots of <u>energy</u>, most of which comes from <u>burning fossil fuels</u>. So recycling metals uses less of our <u>limited resources</u> of fossil fuels and means less CO_2 is released.

2) **Paper** Paper is produced from <u>wood</u>. <u>Recycling paper</u> means that <u>fewer trees</u> have to be <u>cut down</u>, which helps to <u>prevent deforestation</u> (see p.24). <u>Recycling paper</u> uses <u>28%-70% less energy</u> than manufacturing new paper.

3) **Plastics** Most plastics are made from <u>crude oil</u> — so recycling plastics helps to <u>conserve</u> our <u>oil resources</u>. Plastics are really <u>slow to decompose</u> — if they're thrown away (rather than recycled), they take up space in landfill sites for years.

4) **Glass** Glass is <u>manufactured</u> from various <u>raw materials</u> (e.g. sand, limestone). Recycling glass <u>saves our resources</u>, e.g. making new glass needs <u>much higher temperatures</u> (and uses <u>more fuel</u>) than recycling glass. Recycled glass is <u>just as good quality</u> as new glass.

There are Some Problems with Recycling

1) Recycling still <u>uses energy</u>, e.g. for <u>collecting</u>, <u>sorting</u>, <u>cleaning</u> and <u>processing waste</u>.

2) Some waste materials can be difficult and <u>time-consuming to sort</u> out, e.g. different types of <u>plastic</u> have to be separated from each other before they can be recycled.

3) The <u>equipment needed</u> for recycling can be <u>expensive</u>, e.g. equipment for sorting plastics automatically.

4) In some cases, the <u>quality</u> of recycled materials <u>isn't as good</u> as new materials, e.g. recycled paper.

5) <u>Some materials</u> can only be <u>recycled</u> a <u>limited number of times</u> (e.g. plastics, paper). Others can be recycled indefinitely though (e.g. aluminium).

The UK Produces a Lot of Waste — and Could Recycle More

1) England and Wales produce over <u>100 million tonnes</u> of domestic, commercial and industrial <u>waste</u> a year.

2) The amount of waste <u>recycled</u> in the UK is <u>increasing</u> — but it's still not as much as some other European countries. E.g. this table shows the percentage of packaging material recycled.

3) <u>New laws</u> are being introduced in the UK and the European Union (EU) to <u>increase recycling</u>, e.g. by 2015, EU law requires that cars will have to be made of 95% recyclable materials.

Country	% of packaging material recycled
Belgium	70
Germany	75
Italy	46
Netherlands	51
Spain	44
UK	42

Recycling — doing the Tour de France twice...

Recycling isn't perfect — but it's generally a lot better than dumping all our rubbish in a big hole in the ground. Do your bit — <u>reuse plastic bags</u> and <u>recycle your drinks cans</u>.

Revision Summary for B2 Topic 4

Here goes, folks — another beautiful page of revision questions to keep you at your desk studying hard until your parents have gone out and you can finally nip downstairs to watch TV. Think twice though before you reach for that remote control. These questions are actually pretty good — certainly more entertaining than 'Train Your Husband Like He's a Dog' or 'Celebrities Dance Around'. Question 14 is almost as good as an episode of 'Supernanny'. Question 4 is the corker though — like a reunion episode of 'Friends' but a lot funnier. Give the questions a go. Oh go on.

1) Give three factors which affect the distribution and size of a population in a particular environment.
2) Why is having a territory important for some animals?
3) This is a food web in a pond:

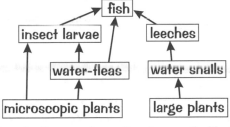

    a) The leeches in the pond die. Is the number of water snails likely to increase or decrease? Give a reason for your answer.
    b) Which two organisms are competing to eat the water-fleas?
4) Explain two ways that deep-sea fish have adapted to their habitat.
5) Why are there no plants in a deep-sea habitat?
6) Give an example of how animals have adapted to living at high altitudes.
7) Give four ways in which human activity releases carbon dioxide into the Earth's atmosphere.
8) What is the purpose of catalytic converters?
9) Why is there debate about how to interpret data on global warming?
10) Which gases cause acid rain? How are these produced?
11) Describe the damage which can be caused by acid rain.
12) How do fertilisers and sewage cause water pollution?
13) Describe two ways in which water pollution can be measured.
14) What type of pollution are lichen very sensitive to?
15) What can be used as a living indicator of ozone layer depletion?
16) How do CFCs affect the ozone layer?
17) Explain four reasons why conservation of habitats and species is important.
18) How can conservation lead to greater biodiversity?
19) What is coppicing?
20) Give two advantages and two disadvantages of recycling.
21) Give four types of material which can be recycled.
22) Give an example of what is being done to increase the amount of recycling.

Balancing Equations

Equations need practice if you're going to get them right, and you'll need them all through Chemistry. Every time you do an equation you need to practise getting it right rather than skating over it.

The Symbol Equation Shows the Atoms on Both Sides:

A chemical reaction can be described by the process REACTANTS → PRODUCTS.

e.g. magnesium reacts with oxygen to produce magnesium oxide.

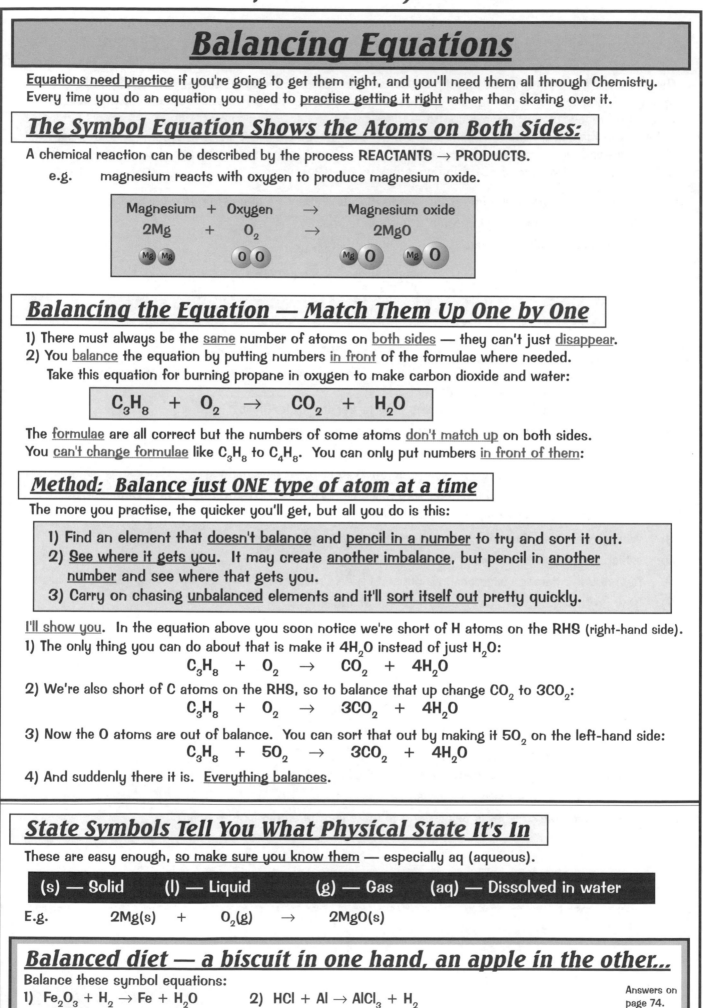

Magnesium	+	Oxygen	→	Magnesium oxide
$2Mg$	+	O_2	→	$2MgO$

Balancing the Equation — Match Them Up One by One

1) There must always be the same number of atoms on both sides — they can't just disappear.
2) You balance the equation by putting numbers in front of the formulae where needed.

Take this equation for burning propane in oxygen to make carbon dioxide and water:

$$C_3H_8 + O_2 \rightarrow CO_2 + H_2O$$

The formulae are all correct but the numbers of some atoms don't match up on both sides. You can't change formulae like C_3H_8 to C_4H_8. You can only put numbers in front of them:

Method: Balance just ONE type of atom at a time

The more you practise, the quicker you'll get, but all you do is this:

> 1) Find an element that doesn't balance and pencil in a number to try and sort it out.
> 2) See where it gets you. It may create another imbalance, but pencil in another number and see where that gets you.
> 3) Carry on chasing unbalanced elements and it'll sort itself out pretty quickly.

I'll show you. In the equation above you soon notice we're short of H atoms on the RHS (right-hand side).
1) The only thing you can do about that is make it $4H_2O$ instead of just H_2O:
$$C_3H_8 + O_2 \rightarrow CO_2 + 4H_2O$$

2) We're also short of C atoms on the RHS, so to balance that up change CO_2 to $3CO_2$:
$$C_3H_8 + O_2 \rightarrow 3CO_2 + 4H_2O$$

3) Now the O atoms are out of balance. You can sort that out by making it $5O_2$ on the left-hand side:
$$C_3H_8 + 5O_2 \rightarrow 3CO_2 + 4H_2O$$

4) And suddenly there it is. Everything balances.

State Symbols Tell You What Physical State It's In

These are easy enough, so make sure you know them — especially aq (aqueous).

(s) — Solid	(l) — Liquid	(g) — Gas	(aq) — Dissolved in water

E.g. $2Mg(s) + O_2(g) \rightarrow 2MgO(s)$

Balanced diet — a biscuit in one hand, an apple in the other...

Balance these symbol equations:
1) $Fe_2O_3 + H_2 \rightarrow Fe + H_2O$
2) $HCl + Al \rightarrow AlCl_3 + H_2$

Answers on page 74.

Crude Oil

Nothing as amazingly useful as crude oil would be without its problems. No, that'd be too good to be true.

Crude Oil Provides an Important Fuel for Modern Life

1) Crude oil fractions (e.g. petrol, diesel, kerosene) burn cleanly, so they make good <u>fuels</u>. Most modern transport is fuelled by a crude oil fraction, e.g. cars, boats, trains and planes. Gas and oil are also burnt in <u>central heating</u> in homes, and in <u>power stations</u> to <u>generate electricity</u>.

2) Often there are <u>alternatives</u> to using crude oil fractions as fuel, e.g. electricity can be generated by <u>nuclear</u> power or <u>wind</u> power, there are <u>ethanol</u> powered cars, and <u>solar</u> energy can be used to heat water.

3) But things tend to be <u>set up</u> for using oil fractions. For example, cars are designed for <u>petrol or diesel</u> and they're <u>readily available</u>. There are filling stations all over the country, with specially designed storage facilities and pumps. So crude oil fractions are often the <u>easiest and cheapest</u> things to use.

4) Crude oil fractions are often <u>more reliable</u> too — e.g. solar and wind power need the right weather conditions. Nuclear energy is reliable, but there are lots of concerns about its <u>safety</u>.

It Also Provides Raw Materials for Plastics and Chemicals

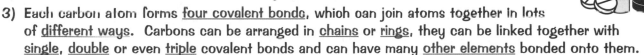

1) As well as fuels, crude oil provides the raw materials for making various <u>chemicals</u>, including <u>plastics</u>, <u>paints</u>, <u>solvents</u>, <u>detergents</u> and lots of <u>medicines</u>.

2) Crude oil is so useful because it's mainly <u>carbon</u>.

3) Each carbon atom forms <u>four covalent bonds</u>, which can join atoms together in lots of <u>different ways</u>. Carbons can be arranged in <u>chains</u> or <u>rings</u>, they can be linked together with <u>single</u>, <u>double</u> or even <u>triple</u> covalent bonds and can have many <u>other elements</u> bonded onto them.

4) Unlike most other elements, carbon can form <u>huge molecules</u> containing hundreds of atoms joined together, e.g. the <u>hormone insulin</u> $C_{257}H_{383}N_{65}O_{77}S_6$, as well as many different <u>plastics</u> (see page 43).

5) Without the <u>variety</u> of compounds that it's possible to form with carbon, <u>complicated life forms</u> such as plants and animals probably wouldn't exist.

But It Might Run Out One Day...Eeek

1) Most scientists think that oil will <u>run out</u>. But no one knows exactly when.

2) There have been heaps of <u>different predictions</u> — e.g. about 40 years ago, scientists predicted that it'd all be gone by the year 2000.

3) <u>New oil reserves</u> are discovered from time to time — e.g. four new oil fields were found in Oman in the Middle East in February 2006. No one knows <u>how much</u> oil will be discovered in the future though.

4) Also, <u>technology</u> is constantly improving, so it's now possible to extract oil that was once too <u>difficult</u> or <u>expensive</u> to extract. It's likely that technology will improve further — but who knows how much?

5) In the <u>worst-case scenario</u>, oil may be gone in about 25 years — and that's not far off.

6) Some people think we should <u>immediately stop</u> using oil for things like transport, for which there are alternatives, and keep it for things that it's absolutely <u>essential</u> for, like some chemicals and medicines.

7) It will take time to <u>develop</u> alternative fuels to satisfy all our energy needs and to <u>adapt things</u> so the fuels can be used on a wide scale, e.g. to design new car engines or special storage tanks.

8) So however long oil does last for, it's a good idea to start <u>conserving</u> it and finding <u>alternatives</u> now.

If oil alternatives aren't developed, we might get caught short...

Crude oil is <u>really important</u> to our lives. Take <u>petrol</u> for instance — at the first whisper of a shortage, there's mayhem. Loads of people dash to the petrol station and start filling up their tanks. This causes a queue, which starts everyone else panicking. I don't know what they'll do when it runs out totally.

Alkanes and Alkenes

When you crack crude oil (next page) you get <u>alkanes</u> and <u>alkenes</u>. Know the differences between them.

ALKANES Have All C–C SINGLE Bonds

1) They're made up of <u>chains</u> of carbon atoms with <u>single</u> covalent bonds between them.
2) They're called <u>saturated</u> hydrocarbons because they have <u>no</u> spare bonds.
3) This is also why they <u>don't</u> decolourise <u>bromine water</u> — <u>no</u> spare bonds.
4) They <u>won't</u> form polymers — same reason again, <u>no</u> spare bonds.
5) The first four alkanes are <u>methane</u> (natural gas), <u>ethane</u>, <u>propane</u> and <u>butane</u>.

Bromine water
+ alkane
— still brown.

1) Methane
Formula: CH_4

$$H–C–H \text{ (natural gas)}$$

2) Ethane
Formula: C_2H_6

$$H–C–C–H$$

3) Propane
Formula: C_3H_8

$$H–C–C–C–H$$

4) Butane
Formula: C_4H_{10}

$$H–C–C–C–C–H$$

ALKENES Have a C=C DOUBLE Bond

1) They're <u>chains</u> of carbon atoms with some <u>double</u> bonds.
2) They are called <u>unsaturated</u> hydrocarbons because they have some 'spare' bonds left.
3) This is why they will decolourise <u>bromine water</u>. They form <u>bonds</u> with bromine atoms.
4) They form <u>polymers</u> by <u>opening up</u> their double bonds to 'hold hands' in a long chain.
5) The first two alkenes are <u>ethene</u> and <u>propene</u>.

Bromine water
+ alkene —
decolourised

1) Ethene
Formula: C_2H_4

$$C=C$$

2) Propene
Formula: C_3H_6

$$H–C–C=C$$

Notice the names: "<u>meth-</u>" means "<u>one carbon atom</u>", "<u>eth-</u>" means "<u>two C atoms</u>", "<u>prop-</u>" means "<u>three C atoms</u>", "<u>but-</u>" means "<u>four C atoms</u>", etc. The only difference then between the names of <u>alkanes</u> and <u>alkenes</u> is just the "<u>-ane</u>" or "<u>-ene</u>" on the end.

Alkenes React with Water to Make Alcohols

1) This is how <u>alcohols</u> are commonly made <u>industrially</u> — using a process called <u>hydration</u>.
2) Ethene, made during the cracking of crude oil, reacts with steam at <u>300 °C</u> and a pressure of <u>70 atmospheres</u>, using <u>phosphoric acid</u> as a catalyst.
3) The product is <u>ethanol</u>.

$$C=C + H_2O \longrightarrow H–C–C–O–H$$

Alkane anybody who doesn't learn this lot properly...

Hydrating alkenes is a good way to produce industrial alcohol because it needs to be very <u>pure</u>. You can also make alcohol by fermenting sugar then distilling the product, but you can't get it as pure that way.

Cracking Hydrocarbons

Cracking — Splitting Up Long-Chain Hydrocarbons

1) Long-chain hydrocarbons form thick gloopy liquids like tar which aren't all that useful.

2) The process called cracking turns them into shorter molecules which are much more useful.

3) Cracking is a form of thermal decomposition, which just means breaking molecules down into simpler molecules by heating them.

4) A lot of the longer molecules produced from fractional distillation are cracked into smaller ones because there's more demand for products like petrol than for diesel or lubricating oil.

5) More importantly, cracking produces alkenes, which are needed for making plastics.

Conditions for Cracking: Heat, Plus a Catalyst

In industry, vaporised hydrocarbons are passed over a powdered catalyst at about 400 °C – 700 °C. Silicon dioxide (SiO_2) and aluminium oxide (Al_2O_3) are used as catalysts.

In the lab, you can use porcelain as a catalyst for the reaction:

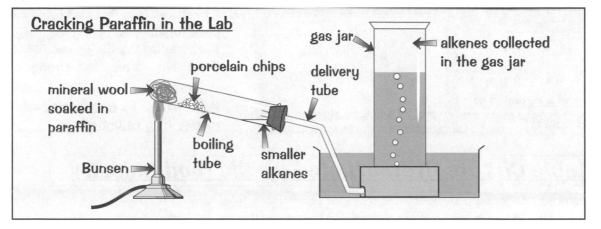

Cracking Paraffin in the Lab

1) Start by heating the paraffin. After a few seconds, move the Bunsen burner to heat the porcelain chips. Alternate between the two until the paraffin vaporises and the porcelain glows red.

2) The heated paraffin vapour cracks as it passes over the heated porcelain.

3) Small alkanes collect at the end of the boiling tube, while alkene gases travel down the delivery tube.

4) The alkenes are then collected through water using a gas jar.

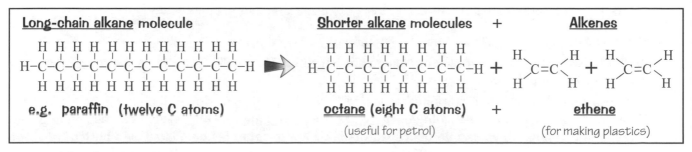

Bunsen and a boiling tube — cracking paraffin-alia...

So, cracking's useful for two things — making alkenes for plastics, and turning bitumen and candle wax (of limited use) into things like petrol and cooking gas (which are really rather handy). Learn that apparatus, and the method for cracking paraffin. Cover the page, scribble it all down, check, try again...

Vegetable Oils

Oils can be saturated (no C-C double bonds — see p.40), monounsaturated or polyunsaturated.

Vegetable Oils are Usually Unsaturated

Unsaturated compounds are ones that contain carbon-carbon double bonds (like alkenes, see p.40).

> MONO means one. An oil molecule with only one carbon-carbon double bond is monounsaturated.
> POLY means many. If an oil molecule has more than one double bond, it's polyunsaturated.

1) The sort of oils that you eat in your food can be important for your health.

2) Polyunsaturated oils are thought to be the healthiest and saturated oils the least healthy, because of what they do to the amount of cholesterol in your blood.

3) Cholesterol is a fatty substance that's made in the liver. High levels of cholesterol in the blood are linked to an increased risk of heart disease.

4) You can reduce the level of cholesterol in your blood and so reduce your risk of heart disease by eating polyunsaturated oils in place of saturated oils.

Unsaturated Oils are Runnier than Saturated Ones

1) Double bonds change the shape of molecules by making an inflexible 'kink' in the carbon chain.

part of a saturated oil

part of a polyunsaturated oil

2) Kinked and less flexible chains can't pack together as tightly as straighter, flexible ones, so the forces between the molecules aren't as strong.

3) Weaker forces make oils less viscous (less thick). So unsaturated oils are runnier than saturated oils.

Vegetable Oils are Hydrogenated for the Food Industry

1) Unsaturated oils (ones with double bonds) can be changed to saturated oils by breaking a double bond and adding hydrogen — a process called hydrogenation.

2) A nickel catalyst is needed to help the reaction along:

part of an unsaturated oil

part of a saturated oil

3) The nickel catalyst is a solid and can be filtered out and used again.

4) As the filtered oil cools down to room temperature it turns into a solid fat (a fat is just an oil that is solid at room temperature).

5) Polyunsaturated vegetable oils are hydrogenated to make margarine. Not all the double bonds in the oil are hydrogenated, so some of the margarine is still unsaturated — it's called a partially hydrogenated oil. It's firm enough to spread on your toast, but still low in saturates compared with butter.

What do you call a parrot in a raincoat? Polyunsaturated...

Some of the double bonds that are left in partially hydrogenated vegetable oils get a bit 'mangled' and you end up with things called trans fats. Most trans fats are completely artificial (you don't get them in nature), and studies have linked them to an increased risk of heart disease.

Plastics

Plastics are made up of lots of small molecules joined together.

Plastics are Long-Chain Molecules Called Polymers

1) Plastics are formed when lots of small molecules called monomers join together to give a polymer.
2) There are two basic types of polymer — addition and condensation. Addition polymerisation only makes one product (see below). Condensation polymerisation makes two — the polymer and a simple compound like water or HCl. You don't need to know any details about condensation polymers, though.

Addition Polymers are Made Under High Pressure

The monomers that make up addition polymers have a carbon double bond — they're unsaturated.

Under high pressure and with a catalyst to help them along, many unsaturated small molecules will open up those double bonds and 'join hands' (polymerise) to form very long saturated chains — polymers.

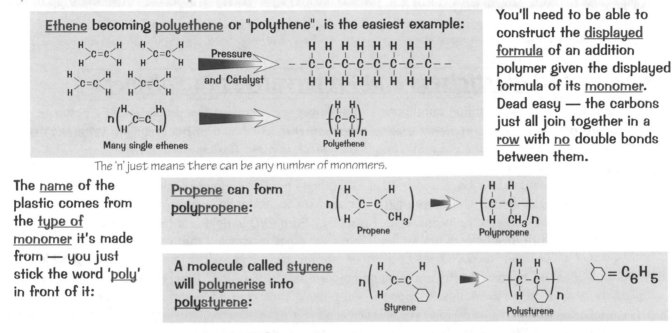

Ethene becoming polyethene or "polythene", is the easiest example:

Many single ethenes → Polyethene

The 'n' just means there can be any number of monomers.

You'll need to be able to construct the displayed formula of an addition polymer given the displayed formula of its monomer. Dead easy — the carbons just all join together in a row with no double bonds between them.

The name of the plastic comes from the type of monomer it's made from — you just stick the word 'poly' in front of it:

Propene can form polypropene:

Propene → Polypropene

A molecule called styrene will polymerise into polystyrene:

$\bigcirc = C_6H_5$

Styrene → Polystyrene

Most Plastics Don't Rot, so They're Hard to Get Rid Of

1) UK households produce over 2 million tonnes of plastic waste every year — so it's a big problem.
2) Toxic gases are given off if you burn plastic, so that's not a good idea.
3) It's best to recycle them as this helps to conserve resources. Recycling is expensive and difficult though — there are lots of types of plastic which have to be separated before recycling.
4) Most plastics are 'non-biodegradable' — they're not broken down by microorganisms, so they don't rot. If you bury them in a landfill site, they'll still be there years later.
5) Some polythene bags are now made with starch granules in them. If the plastic is buried, the starch is broken down by microorganisms in the soil, and the bag breaks up into tiny pieces of polythene.
6) There are currently some fully biodegradable plastics, but they're about 10 times more expensive than ordinary ones. Scientists are working on genetically modifying plants to produce the raw materials for more biodegradable plastics. With any new product like this tests have to be done to find out exactly what happens when the plastic breaks down to make sure that nothing harmful is produced.
7) You can also get plastics that break down in sunlight — they tend to be used in agriculture.

You're not done yet — more plasticky goodness over the page...

Getting rid of plastic is a big problem, but recycling can help. There are recycling points all around the country for plastic bottles, and many supermarkets collect old polythene bags for recycling.

Plastics

Forces Between Molecules Determine the Properties of Plastics

Strong covalent bonds hold the atoms together in long chains. But it's the bonds between the different molecule chains that determine the properties of the plastic.

Weak Forces:
Long chains held together by weak forces are free to slide over each other.

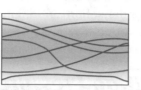

THERMOPLASTIC POLYMERS, like polythene, don't have cross-linking between chains. The forces between the chains are really easy to overcome, so it's dead easy to melt the plastic. When it cools, the thermoplastic hardens into a new shape. You can melt these plastics and remould them as many times as you like.

Strong Forces:
Some plastics have stronger bonds between the polymer chains, called crosslinks, that hold the chains firmly together.

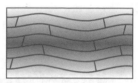

THERMOSETTING POLYMERS, like Bakelite, have crosslinks. These hold the chains together in a solid structure. The polymer doesn't soften when it's heated — but too much heat makes it burn. Thermosetting polymers are the tough guys of the plastic world. They're strong, hard and rigid.

You Can Add Plasticisers and Preservatives to Polymers

1) The starting materials, reaction conditions and additives will all affect the properties of a polymer.

2) Using styrene as a starting material produces polystyrene, which is a brittle polymer. Whereas using ethene as a starting material will make polythene, which is more flexible (see p.43).

3) Polythene can be made by heating ethene to about 200 °C under high pressure. This makes the light, flexible polythene used for bags and bottles. Polythene made at a lower temperature and pressure (with a catalyst) is denser and more rigid. It's used for water tanks and drainpipes.

4) Additives can also change the properties of plastics. Pure PVC is rigid and brittle at room temperature. To make PVC cloth, plasticisers are added. These are small molecules that get between the polymer chains and allow them to move past each other more easily. This makes the plastic more flexible.

5) Many plastics will become brittle and change colour if left in the Sun. Preservatives can be added to plastics such as uPVC in window frames to help prolong their useful life and appearance.

The Use of a Plastic Depends on Its Properties

You've got to be able to answer a question like this one in the exam.

Choose from the table the plastic that would be best suited for making:

a) a disposable cup for hot drinks,

b) clothing,

c) a measuring cylinder.

Give reasons for each choice.

Plastic	Cost	Resistance to chemicals	Melting point	Transparency	Rigidity	Can be made into fibres
W	High	High	High	Low	High	No
X	Low	Low	Low	Low	Low	Yes
Y	High	High	High	High	High	No
Z	Low	Low	High	High	High	No

Answers

a) **Z** — low cost (disposable) and high melting point (for hot drinks),

b) **X** — flexible (essential for clothing) and able to be made into fibres (clothing is usually woven),

c) **Y** — transparent and resistant to chemicals (you need to be able to see the liquid inside and the liquid and measuring cylinder mustn't react with each other).

Platinum cards — my favourite sort of plastic...

You don't have to learn the properties of different plastics — you'll be given those in the exam — you just need to think about which properties are good for which uses. It's just common sense.

Drug Synthesis

Chemists Don't Just Guess

1) When chemists are making new chemicals, they use information about known reactions. The type of reaction below is called esterification (don't worry, you don't need to learn it — it's just an example):

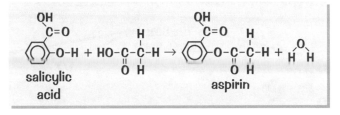

2) Chemists can use this known reaction to predict what would be made in a similar unknown one.

3) Salicylic acid is a substance known to help with lowering fevers and relieving pain but which can cause ulcers of the mouth and stomach. Using esterification you can make a new compound, aspirin, which still works but causes milder side effects.

New Drugs Have to be Safe

Before a drug can be marketed it has to go through many stages of testing:

1) Tests on cultures of living cells and animals help to make sure the drug works, and isn't toxic. After that come several stages of human trials.

2) In Phase I, the drug is tested on human volunteers. They're usually healthy people and the doses given are very small, gradually building up to the required level (under the supervision of a doctor).

3) In Phase II small numbers of people actually suffering from the disease are treated.

4) In Phase III larger groups are tested. Some patients are given the drug while others are given a harmless tablet without the drug (a placebo). The results have to be carefully analysed to see if the drug is working and to look for any dangerous or unpleasant side effects.

5) This process can take over 10 years and cost several hundred million pounds. Ouch.

Drugs are Developed Using Staged Synthesis

Imagine A, B, C and D represent chemicals that can react with each other to make a new compound ABCD. You can make the new compound in stages, like this:
A + B → AB, then AB + C → ABC, then ABC + D → ABCD

When a company is trying to find a new drug, it likes to have lots of possible substances to test. Staged synthesis is a way of making lots of similar substances, very quickly.

To make a 'family' of compounds similar to ABCD, a drug company would react a family of substances similar to A (call them A_1, A_2, etc.) with a family similar to B (B_1, B_2, etc.) and so on...
They're reacted in such a way as to give every possible combination, e.g:

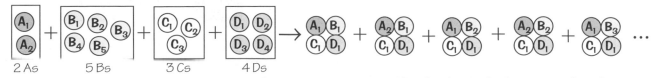

You can calculate the total number of products from a reaction like this by multiplying together the number of reactants in each family, i.e. the numbers of As, Bs, Cs and Ds involved in the reaction. So in this example, you would end up with $2 \times 5 \times 3 \times 4 = \underline{120 \text{ different products}}$.

What a page — it's enough to give you a headache...

And once they've got all those compounds, they can test each one to see which works best. Cunning.

Relative Formula Mass

The biggest trouble with <u>relative atomic mass</u> and <u>relative formula mass</u> is that they <u>sound</u> so blood-curdling. Take a few deep breaths, and just enjoy, as the mists slowly clear...

Relative Atomic Mass, A_r — Easy Peasy

1) This is just a way of saying how <u>heavy</u> different atoms are <u>compared</u> with the mass of an atom of carbon-12. So carbon-12 has A_r of <u>exactly 12</u>.

2) It turns out that the <u>relative atomic mass</u> A_r is usually just the same as the <u>mass number</u> of the element (to the nearest whole number). There's more about mass number on page 52.

3) In the periodic table, the elements all have <u>two</u> numbers. The <u>smaller one</u> is the <u>atomic number</u> (how many protons it has). The <u>bigger one</u> is the <u>relative atomic mass</u>. Easy peasy, I'd say.

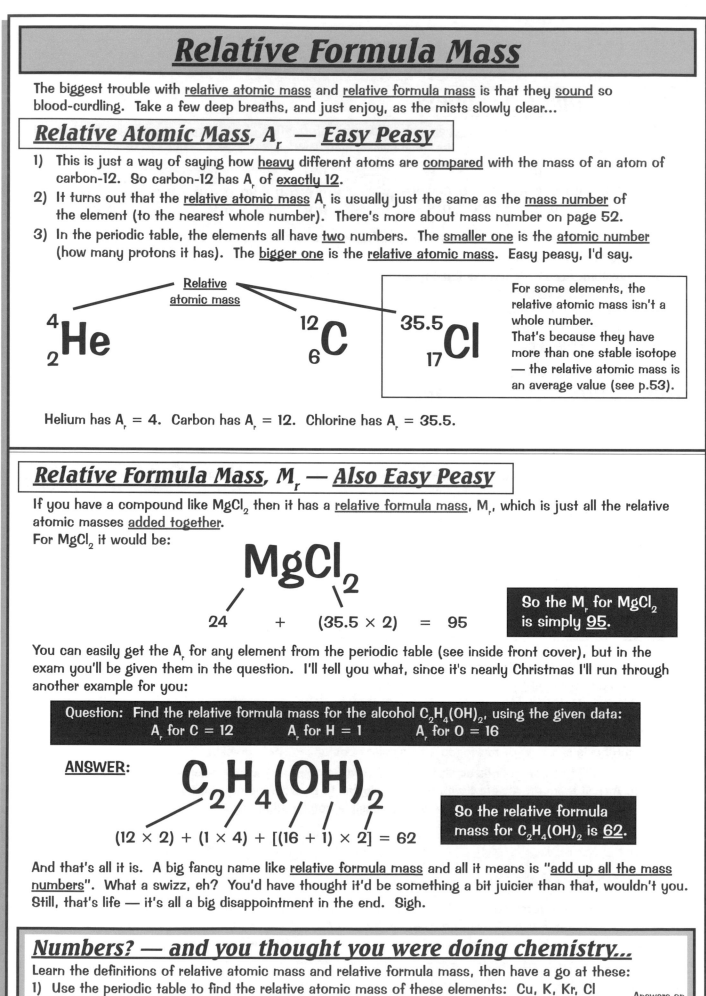

Relative atomic mass

^4_2He $^{12}_6\text{C}$ $^{35.5}_{17}\text{Cl}$

For some elements, the relative atomic mass isn't a whole number. That's because they have more than one stable isotope — the relative atomic mass is an average value (see p.53).

Helium has A_r = 4. Carbon has A_r = 12. Chlorine has A_r = 35.5.

Relative Formula Mass, M_r — Also Easy Peasy

If you have a compound like $MgCl_2$ then it has a <u>relative formula mass</u>, M_r, which is just all the relative atomic masses <u>added together</u>.
For $MgCl_2$ it would be:

$$MgCl_2$$
$$24 \quad + \quad (35.5 \times 2) \quad = \quad 95$$

So the M_r for $MgCl_2$ is simply <u>95</u>.

You can easily get the A_r for any element from the periodic table (see inside front cover), but in the exam you'll be given them in the question. I'll tell you what, since it's nearly Christmas I'll run through another example for you:

Question: Find the relative formula mass for the alcohol $C_2H_4(OH)_2$, using the given data:
A_r for C = 12 A_r for H = 1 A_r for O = 16

<u>ANSWER:</u>
$$C_2H_4(OH)_2$$
$$(12 \times 2) + (1 \times 4) + [(16 + 1) \times 2] = 62$$

So the relative formula mass for $C_2H_4(OH)_2$ is <u>62</u>.

And that's all it is. A big fancy name like <u>relative formula mass</u> and all it means is "<u>add up all the mass numbers</u>". What a swizz, eh? You'd have thought it'd be something a bit juicier than that, wouldn't you. Still, that's life — it's all a big disappointment in the end. Sigh.

Numbers? — and you thought you were doing chemistry...

Learn the definitions of relative atomic mass and relative formula mass, then have a go at these:
1) Use the periodic table to find the relative atomic mass of these elements: Cu, K, Kr, Cl
2) Also find the relative formula mass of these compounds: NaOH, Fe_2O_3, C_6H_{14}, $Mg(NO_3)_2$

Answers on page 74.

Empirical Formulae

Although relative atomic mass and relative formula mass are easy enough, it can get just a tad trickier when you start getting into other calculations which use them. It depends on how good your maths is basically, because it's all to do with ratios and percentages.

Finding the Empirical Formula (from Masses or Percentages)

This sounds a lot worse than it really is. All 'empirical' means is that it's a formula based on an experimental method, rather than theory.

Try this for an easy peasy stepwise method for calculating an empirical formula:

1) List all the elements in the compound (there are usually only two or three!)
2) Underneath them, write their experimental masses or percentages.
3) Divide each mass or percentage by the A_r for that particular element.
4) Turn the numbers you get into a nice simple ratio by multiplying and/or dividing them by well-chosen numbers.
5) Get the ratio in its simplest form, and that tells you the empirical formula of the compound.

Example: Find the empirical formula of the iron oxide produced when 44.8 g of iron react with 19.2 g of oxygen. (A_r for iron = 56, A_r for oxygen = 16)

Method:
1) List the two elements: Fe   O
2) Write in the experimental masses: 44.8   19.2
3) Divide by the A_r for each element: $44.8/56 = 0.8$ $19.2/16 = 1.2$
4) Multiply by 10...   8   12
     ...then divide by 4:   2   3
5) So the simplest formula is 2 atoms of Fe to 3 atoms of O, i.e. Fe_2O_3. And that's it done.

You need to realise (for the exam) that this empirical method (i.e. based on experiment) is the only way of finding out the formula of a compound. Rust is iron oxide, sure, but is it FeO, or Fe_2O_3? Only an experiment to determine the empirical formula will tell you for certain.

The Empirical Formula isn't Always the Same as the Molecular Formula

The empirical formula of a compound is the simplest formula that tells you the ratio of different elements in the compound.

The molecular formula of a compound tells you the actual number of atoms of each element in a single molecule.

So that means ethene (C_2H_4), propene (C_3H_6) and all the other alkenes have the same empirical formula (CH_2) but different molecular formulae.

The molecular formulae are all whole number multiples of the empirical formula.

With this empirical formula I can rule the world! — mwa ha ha...

Make sure you learn the five steps in the top red box. Then try this example:
   Find the empirical formula when 2.4 g of carbon reacts with 0.8 g of hydrogen.   Answer on page 74.

Calculating Masses in Reactions

These can be kinda scary too, but chill out, little trembling one — just relax and enjoy.

The Three Important Steps — Not to be Missed...

(Miss one out and it'll all go horribly wrong, believe me.)

> 1) <u>Write out</u> the balanced <u>equation</u>.
> 2) <u>Work out</u> M$_r$ — just for the <u>two bits you want</u>.
> 3) Apply the rule: <u>Divide to get one, then multiply to get all</u>.
> (But you have to apply this first to the substance they give information about, and then the other one!)

Don't worry — these steps should all make sense when you look at the example below.

<u>Example:</u> What mass of magnesium oxide is produced when 60 g of magnesium is burned in air?

<u>Answer:</u>

1) Write out the balanced equation:

$$2Mg + O_2 \rightarrow 2MgO$$

2) Work out the relative formula masses:

(don't do the oxygen — you don't need it)

$$2 \times 24 \rightarrow 2 \times (24 + 16)$$
$$48 \rightarrow 80$$

3) Apply the rule: <u>Divide to get one, then multiply to get all</u>.

The two numbers, 48 and 80, tell us that 48 g of Mg react to give 80 g of MgO.
Here's the tricky bit. You've now got to be able to write this down:

> 48 g of Mg ......reacts to give.....80 g of MgO
>
> 1 g of Mg ......reacts to give.....
>
> 60 g of Mg .....reacts to give......

<u>The big clue</u> is that in the question they've said that "<u>60 g of magnesium</u>" is burnt,
i.e. they've told us how much <u>magnesium</u> to have, and that's how you know to fill in the <u>left-hand side</u>
of the box first, because:

> We'll first need to ÷ by 48 to get 1 g of Mg
> and then need to × by 60 to get 60 g of Mg.

<u>Then</u> you can work out the numbers on the other side (shown in red below) by realising that you must <u>divide both sides by 48</u> and then <u>multiply both sides by 60</u>. It's tricky.

$$
\begin{array}{l}
\div 48 \left\{ \begin{array}{l} 48 \text{ g of Mg } \dots\dots 80 \text{ g of MgO} \\ 1 \text{ g of Mg } \dots\dots 1.67 \text{ g of MgO} \end{array} \right\} \div 48 \\
\times 60 \left\{ \begin{array}{l} 60 \text{ g of Mg } \dots\dots 100 \text{ g of MgO} \end{array} \right. \times 60
\end{array}
$$

The mass of product is called the <u>yield</u> of a reaction. Masses you calculate in this way are called <u>THEORETICAL YIELDS</u>.
<u>In practice</u> you never get 100% of the yield, so the amount of product will be <u>less than calculated</u> (see p. 50).

This finally tells us that <u>60 g of magnesium will produce 100 g of magnesium oxide</u>.
If the question had said, "Find how much magnesium gives 500 g of magnesium oxide", you'd fill in the MgO side first instead, <u>because that's the one you'd have the information about</u>. Got it? Good-O!

Reaction mass calculations — no worries, matey...

The only way to get good at these is to <u>practise</u>. So make sure you can do the example, then try these:
1) Find the mass of calcium which gives 30 g of calcium oxide (CaO) when burnt in air.
2) What mass of fluorine fully reacts with potassium to make 116 g of potassium fluoride (KF)?

Answers on page 74.

Atom Economy

In industrial reactions, you want as much of your raw materials as possible to get turned into useful stuff. This depends on the <u>atom economy</u> and the <u>percentage yield</u> (see next page) of the reaction.

"Atom Economy" — % of Reactants Changed to Useful Products

1) A lot of reactions make <u>more than one product</u>. Some of them will be <u>useful</u>, but others will just be <u>waste</u>, e.g. when you make quicklime from limestone, you also get CO_2 as a waste product.

2) The <u>atom economy</u> of a reaction tells you how much of the <u>mass</u> of the reactants ends up as useful products. <u>Learn</u> the equation:

$$\text{atom economy} = \frac{\text{total } M_r \text{ of useful products}}{\text{total } M_r \text{ of reactants}} \times 100$$

<u>Example:</u> Hydrogen gas is made on a large scale by reacting natural gas (methane) with steam.

$$CH_4(g) + H_2O(g) \rightarrow CO(g) + 3H_2(g)$$

Calculate the atom economy of this reaction.

<u>Answer:</u> 1) Identify the useful product — that's the hydrogen gas.

2) Work out the M_r of reactants and the useful product:

$$
\begin{array}{ccc}
CH_4 & H_2O & 3H_2 \\
12 + (4 \times 1) & (2 \times 1) + 16 & 3 \times (2 \times 1) \\
34 & & 6
\end{array}
$$

3) Use the formula to calculate the atom economy: $\text{atom economy} = \frac{6}{34} \times 100 = \underline{17.6\%}$

So in this reaction, <u>over 80%</u> of the starting materials are <u>wasted</u>!

In industry, the waste CO is reacted with more steam to make CO_2 (and a bit more H_2). That brings the overall atom economy down to only 15% — but the final waste product is much less nasty that way.

High Atom Economy is Better for Profits and the Environment

1) Pretty obviously, if you're making <u>lots of waste</u>, that's a <u>problem</u>.

2) Reactions with low atom economy use up resources very quickly. At the same time, they make lots of <u>waste</u> materials that have to be <u>disposed</u> of somehow. That tends to make these reactions <u>unsustainable</u> — the raw materials will run out and the waste has to go somewhere.

3) For the same reasons, low atom economy reactions aren't usually <u>profitable</u>. Raw materials are <u>expensive to buy</u>, and waste products can be expensive to <u>remove</u> and dispose of <u>responsibly</u>.

4) One way around the problem is to find a <u>use</u> for the waste products rather than just <u>throwing them away</u>. There's often <u>more than one way</u> to make the product you want, so the trick is to come up with a reaction that gives <u>useful 'by-products'</u> rather than useless ones.

5) That doesn't get round all the problems, though. It can be really hard to separate out the different things made in the reaction to get <u>pure</u> products.

6) The reactions with the <u>highest</u> atom economy are the ones that only have <u>one product</u> — like the Haber process (see page 73). Those reactions have an atom economy of <u>100%</u>.

So why do they make hydrogen in that nasty, inefficient way — well, at the moment it's the best of a bad bunch. The other ways to make hydrogen on an industrial scale, like the electrolysis (see page 60) of salt water, use up massive amounts of energy and are too expensive to be worthwhile.

Atom economy — important, but not the whole story...

You could get asked about <u>any</u> industrial reaction in the exam. Don't panic — whatever example they give you, the <u>same stuff</u> applies. In the real world, high atom economy isn't enough, though. You need to think about the <u>percentage yield</u> of the reaction (next page) and the <u>energy cost</u> as well.

Percentage Yield

Percentage yield tells you about the <u>overall success</u> of an experiment. It compares what you think you should get (<u>theoretical yield</u>) with what you get in practice (<u>actual yield</u>).

Percentage Yield Compares Actual and Theoretical Yield

The more reactants you start with, the higher the <u>actual yield</u> will be — that's pretty obvious. But the <u>percentage yield</u> <u>doesn't</u> depend on the amount of reactants you started with — it's a <u>percentage</u>.

1) The <u>predicted yield</u> of a reaction can be calculated from the <u>balanced reaction equation</u> (see page 48).

2) Percentage yield is given by the formula:

$$\text{percentage yield} = \frac{\text{actual yield (grams)}}{\text{theoretical yield (grams)}} \times 100$$

3) Percentage yield is <u>always</u> somewhere between 0 and 100%.

4) A 100% yield means that you got <u>all</u> the product you expected to get.

5) A 0% yield means that <u>no</u> reactants were converted into product, i.e. no product at all was <u>made</u>.

Yields are Always Less Than 100%

In real life, you <u>never</u> get a 100% yield. Some product or reactant <u>always</u> gets lost along the way — and that goes for big <u>industrial processes</u> as well as school lab experiments.
How this happens depends on <u>what sort of reaction</u> it is and what <u>apparatus</u> is being used.

Lots of things can go wrong, but the four you need to <u>know about</u> are:

1) The Reaction is Reversible

In <u>reversible reactions</u> (like the Haber process — see page 73), not all the reactants change into product.

Instead, you get <u>reactants</u> and <u>products</u> in <u>equilibrium</u>. Changing the conditions moves the <u>equilibrium position</u> (see page 72), so heating the reaction to speed it up might mean a <u>lower yield</u>.

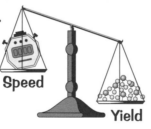

Speed

Yield

3) Transferring Liquids

You always lose a bit of liquid when you <u>transfer</u> it from one container to another — even if you manage not to spill it.

Some of it always gets left behind on the <u>inside surface</u> of the old container. Think about it — it's always wet when you finish.

2) Filtration

When you <u>filter a liquid</u> to remove <u>solid particles</u>, you nearly always lose a bit of liquid or a bit of solid.

1) If you want to <u>keep the liquid</u>, you lose the bit that remains with the solid and filter paper (as they always stay a bit wet).

2) If you want to <u>keep the solid</u>, some of it usually gets left behind when you scrape it off the filter paper — even if you're really careful.

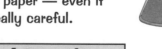

4) Unexpected Reactions

Things don't always go exactly to plan.

Sometimes you get unexpected reactions happening, so the yield of the <u>intended product</u> goes down. These can be caused by <u>impurities</u> in the reactants, but sometimes just changing the <u>reaction conditions</u> affects what products you make.

You can't always get what you want...

A high percentage yield means there's <u>not much waste</u> — which is good for <u>preserving resources</u>, and keeping production <u>costs down</u>. If a reaction's going to be worth doing commercially, it generally has to have a high percentage yield or recyclable reactants, e.g. the Haber process (see page 73).

Revision Summary for C2 Topic 5

There are some tricky bits in that topic, and here are some tricky questions to go with it. The thing is though, why bother doing easy questions? These meaty monsters find out what you really know, and worse, what you really don't. Yeah, I know, it's kinda scary, but if you want to get anywhere in life you've got to face up to a bit of hardship. That's just the way it is. Take a few deep breaths and then try these.

1)* Give three rules for balancing equations, then try balancing these equations:
   a) $CaCO_3 + HCl \rightarrow CaCl_2 + H_2O + CO_2$ b) $Ca + H_2O \rightarrow Ca(OH)_2 + H_2$
   c) $H_2SO_4 + KOH \rightarrow K_2SO_4 + H_2O$ d) $Mg + HNO_3 \rightarrow Mg(NO_3)_2 + H_2$

2) What feature of carbon makes it able to form a very wide range of compounds?

3) Draw out the structural formulae for the first 4 alkanes. Give the name of each compound.

4) Describe what you would see if you added propene to a test tube containing bromine water.

5) How is ethanol made industrially?

6) Draw the apparatus and describe the method used to crack paraffin in the lab.

7)* Complete the balanced symbol equation below (only one product is missing):
$$C_{12}H_{26} \rightarrow C_4H_{10} + \underline{\hspace{1cm}} + C_2H_4$$

8) Define the terms 'saturated', 'monounsaturated' and 'polyunsaturated' for oil molecules.

9) Explain why unsaturated oils are less viscous than saturated ones.

10) What is hydrogenation? What does it do to unsaturated oils?

11) What is a monomer? What is a polymer?

12) Write out the equation for the polymerisation of ethene.

13) Describe some of the problems associated with disposing of plastics.

14) Describe the differences between thermosetting and thermoplastic polymers.
    Explain the differences in terms of the structures of the polymers.

15) Name three factors that affect the properties of a polymer.

16) Why do some plastics have preservatives added?

17)* Alkanes react with chlorine to make compounds called chloroalkanes in reactions like the ones below:
$$CH_4 + Cl_2 \rightarrow CH_3Cl + HCl \qquad C_2H_6 + Cl_2 \rightarrow C_2H_5Cl + HCl$$
    Predict the products of the reaction between propane (C_3H_8) and chlorine.

18) How are drugs tested to make sure they're not toxic to humans?

19)* A family of substances is being synthesised using staged synthesis.
    The process involves two stages — X reacts with Y to form XY, then XY reacts with Z to form XYZ. Given the data in the table, how many possible products are there from this reaction?

Family of reactants	X	Y	Z
Number of reactants in family	7	6	12

20)* Find A_r or M_r for each of these (use the periodic table inside the front cover):
    a) Ca   b) Ag   c) CO_2 d) $MgCO_3$ e) $Al(OH)_3$
    f) ZnO   g) Na_2CO_3 h) sodium chloride

21)* Using the periodic table, find the empirical formula of the compound formed when 227 g of calcium reacts with 216 g of fluorine.

22)*Write down the method for calculating reacting masses.
    a) What mass of magnesium oxide is produced when 112.1 g of magnesium burns in air?
    b) What mass of sodium is needed to produce 108.2 g of sodium oxide?
    c) What mass of carbon will react with hydrogen to produce 24.6 g of propane (C_3H_8)?

23)*Iron is extracted from its ore using carbon monoxide in a process described by this equation:
$$3CO + Fe_2O_3 \rightarrow 3CO_2 + 2Fe$$
    Using the periodic table calculate the atom economy of this reaction.

24) What is the formula for percentage yield? How does percentage yield differ from actual yield?

25) Name four factors that prevent the percentage yield being 100%.

* Answers on page 74

Atoms

There are quite a few different (and equally useful) models of the atom — but chemists tend to like this <u>nuclear model</u> best. You can use it to explain pretty much the whole of Chemistry... which is nice.

The Nucleus

1) It's in the <u>middle</u> of the atom.
2) It contains <u>protons</u> and <u>neutrons</u>.
3) It has a <u>positive charge</u> because of the protons.
4) Almost the <u>whole</u> mass of the atom is <u>concentrated</u> in the nucleus.
5) But size-wise it's <u>tiny</u> compared to the rest of the atom.

The Electrons

1) Move <u>around</u> the nucleus.
2) They're <u>negatively charged</u>.
3) They're <u>tiny</u>, but they cover <u>a lot of space</u>.
4) The <u>size</u> of their orbits determines how big the atom is.
5) They have virtually <u>no</u> mass.
6) They occupy <u>shells</u> around the nucleus.
7) These shells explain <u>the whole of Chemistry</u>.

Atoms are <u>really tiny</u>, don't forget. They're <u>too small to see</u>, even with a microscope.

PARTICLE	RELATIVE MASS	RELATIVE CHARGE
Proton	1	+1
Neutron	1	0
Electron	$\frac{1}{2000}$	–1

<u>Protons</u> are <u>heavy</u> and <u>positively charged</u>.
<u>Neutrons</u> are <u>heavy</u> and <u>neutral</u>.
<u>Electrons</u> are <u>tiny</u> and <u>negatively charged</u>. (Electron mass is often taken as <u>zero</u>.)

Number of Protons Equals Number of Electrons

1) Neutral atoms have <u>no charge</u> overall.
2) The <u>charge</u> on the electrons is the <u>same</u> size as the charge on the <u>protons</u> — but <u>opposite</u>.
3) This means the <u>number</u> of <u>protons</u> always equals the <u>number</u> of <u>electrons</u> in a <u>neutral atom</u>.
4) If some electrons are <u>added or removed</u>, the atom becomes <u>charged</u> and is then an <u>ion</u>.

Atomic Number and Mass Number Describe an Atom

These two numbers tell you how many of each kind of particle an atom has.

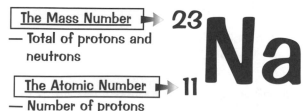

| The Mass Number | ➡ **23** |
— Total of protons and neutrons

| The Atomic Number | ➡ **11** |
— Number of protons

Na

1) The <u>atomic number</u> tells you how many <u>protons</u> there are.
2) Atoms of the <u>same</u> element all have the <u>same</u> number of <u>protons</u> — so atoms of <u>different</u> elements will have <u>different</u> numbers of <u>protons</u>.

3) To get the number of <u>neutrons</u>, just <u>subtract</u> the <u>atomic number</u> from the <u>mass number</u>.
4) The <u>mass number</u> is always the <u>biggest</u> number. On a periodic table, the mass number is actually the <u>relative atomic mass</u>.
5) The <u>mass number</u> tends to be roughly <u>double</u> the <u>atomic</u> number.
6) Which means there's about the <u>same</u> number of protons as neutrons in any nucleus.

Number of protons = number of electrons...

This stuff might seem a bit useless at first, but it should be permanently engraved into your mind. If you don't know these basic facts, you've got no chance of understanding the rest of Chemistry. So <u>learn it now</u>, and watch as the Universe unfolds and reveals its timeless mysteries to you...

Isotopes and Relative Atomic Mass

Some elements have more than one isotope.

Isotopes are the Same Except for an Extra Neutron or Two

A favourite trick exam question: "Explain what is meant by the term isotope"
The trick is that it's impossible to explain what one isotope is. Nice of them that, isn't it!
You have to outsmart them and always start your answer "Isotopes are..."   LEARN the definition:

> **Isotopes are:**   different atomic forms of the **same element**, which have the **SAME** number of **PROTONS** but **DIFFERENT** numbers of **NEUTRONS.**

1) The upshot is: isotopes must have the **same** proton number but **different** mass numbers.

2) If they had **different** proton numbers, they'd be **different** elements altogether.

3) A very popular pair of isotopes are carbon-12 and carbon-14, used for carbon dating.

Carbon-12

$^{12}_{6}C$

6 PROTONS
6 ELECTRONS
6 NEUTRONS

Carbon-14

$^{14}_{6}C$

6 PROTONS
6 ELECTRONS
8 NEUTRONS

The number of electrons decides the chemistry of the element. If the proton number is the same (that is, the number of protons is the same) then the number of electrons must be the same, so the chemistry is the same. The different number of neutrons in the nucleus doesn't affect the chemical behaviour at all.

Relative Atomic Mass Takes All Stable Isotopes into Account

1) Relative atomic mass (A_r) uses the **average mass** of all the isotopes of an element. It has to allow for the **relative mass** of each isotope and its **relative abundance**.

2) Relative abundance just means how much there is of each isotope compared to the **total amount** of the element in the world. This can be a ratio, a fraction or a percentage and is easiest to see with an example:

element	relative mass of isotope	relative abundance
chlorine	35	3
	37	1

This means that there are 2 isotopes of chlorine. One has a relative mass of 35 (^{35}Cl) and the other 37 (^{37}Cl).

The relative abundances show that there are 3 atoms of ^{35}Cl to every 1 of ^{37}Cl.

1) First, multiply the mass of each isotope by its relative abundance.

2) Add those together.

3) Divide by the sum of the relative abundances.

$$A_r = \frac{(35 \times 3) + (37 \times 1)}{3 + 1} = \underline{35.5}$$

Relative atomic masses don't usually come out as whole numbers or easy decimals, but they're often rounded to the nearest 0.5 in periodic tables (see p. 46).

Will this be in your exam? — isotope so...

Some isotopes are unstable. That means they don't stay as they are forever, but change (decay) into other elements. When they do this, they release nuclear radiation (see P2 Topic 11).

The Periodic Table

In 1869, <u>Dmitri Mendeleyev</u> arranged 50 known elements in order of <u>atomic mass</u> to make a Table of Elements. Mendeleyev's table placed elements with <u>similar chemical properties</u> in the same vertical <u>groups</u> — but he found that he had to leave <u>gaps</u> in his table to make this work. The gaps in Medeleyev's table of elements were really clever because they <u>predicted</u> the properties of undiscovered elements. Since then <u>new elements</u> have been found which fit into the gaps left in Mendeleyev's table...

The Periodic Table is a Table of All Known Elements

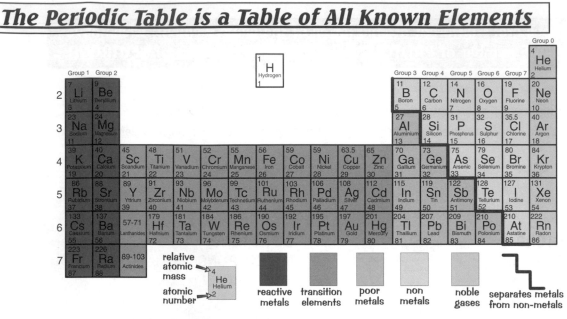

1) We now know there are <u>100ish elements</u> that all materials are made of, with more still being 'discovered'.

2) The <u>modern</u> periodic table shows the elements in order of increasing <u>atomic number</u>.

3) The periodic table is laid out so that elements with <u>similar properties</u> form <u>columns</u>.

4) These <u>vertical columns</u> are called <u>groups</u> and Roman numerals are often (but not always) used for them.

5) The <u>group</u> to which an element belongs <u>corresponds</u> to the <u>number of electrons</u> it has in its <u>outer shell</u>. E.g. Group 1 elements have 1 outer shell electron, Group 2 elements have 2 outer shell electrons and so on.

6) Some of the groups have special names. <u>Group 1</u> elements are called <u>alkali metals</u>. <u>Group 7</u> elements are called <u>halogens</u>, and <u>Group 0</u> are called the <u>noble gases</u>.

Elements in a Group Have the Same Number of Outer Electrons

1) The elements in any one <u>group</u> all have the same number of <u>electrons</u> in their <u>outer shell</u>.

2) That's why they have <u>similar properties</u>. And that's why we arrange them in this way.

3) When only a small number of elements were known, the periodic table was made by looking at the <u>properties</u> of the elements and arranging them in groups — the same groups that they are in today.

4) This idea is <u>extremely important</u> to chemistry — so make sure you understand it.

> The properties of the elements are decided <u>**ENTIRELY**</u> by <u>how many electrons</u> they have.
> <u>Atomic number</u> is therefore very significant because it is equal to the number of electrons each atom has.
>
> But it's the number of electrons in the <u>outer shell</u> which is the really important thing.

I've got a periodic table — Queen Anne legs and everything...

Physicists can produce <u>new</u> elements in particle accelerators, but they're all <u>radioactive</u>. Most only last a fraction of a second before they decay. They haven't even got round to giving most of them proper names yet, but then even "element 114" sounds pretty cool when you say it in Latin — <u>ununquadium</u>...

Electron Shells

The fact that electrons occupy "shells" around the nucleus is what causes the whole of chemistry. Remember that, and watch how it applies to each bit of it. It's ace.

Electron Shell Rules:

1) Electrons always occupy <u>shells</u> (sometimes called <u>energy levels</u>).

2) The <u>lowest</u> energy levels are <u>always filled first</u> — these are the ones closest to the nucleus.

3) Only <u>a certain number</u> of electrons are allowed in each shell:
<u>1st shell:</u>   2   <u>2nd Shell:</u>   8   <u>3rd Shell:</u>   8

4) Atoms are much <u>happier</u> when they have <u>full</u> electron shells — like the <u>noble gases</u> in <u>Group 0</u>.

5) In most atoms the <u>outer shell</u> is <u>not full</u> and this makes the atom want to <u>react</u>.

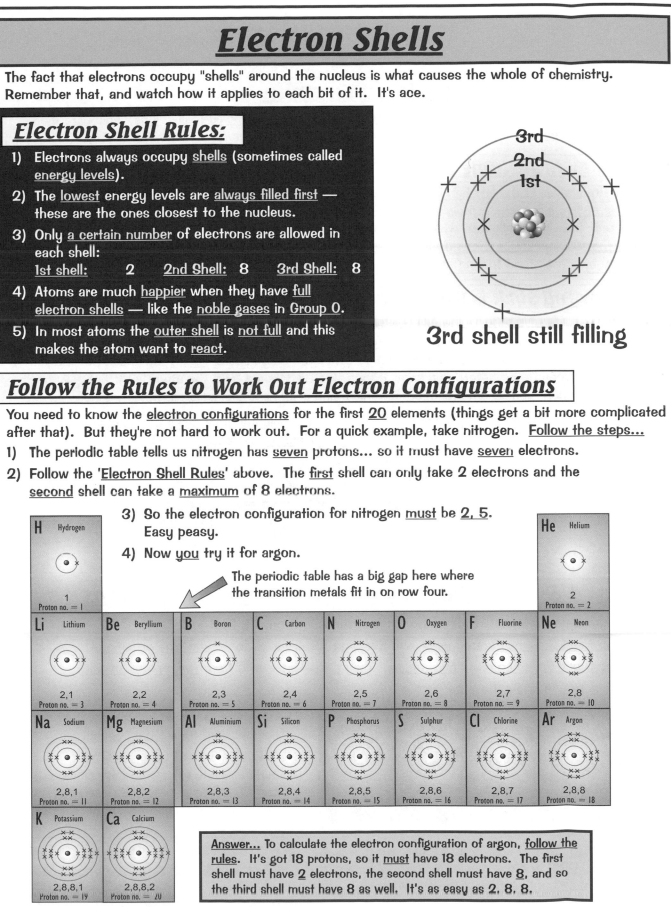

3rd
2nd
1st

3rd shell still filling

Follow the Rules to Work Out Electron Configurations

You need to know the <u>electron configurations</u> for the first <u>20</u> elements (things get a bit more complicated after that). But they're not hard to work out. For a quick example, take nitrogen. <u>Follow the steps...</u>

1) The periodic table tells us nitrogen has <u>seven</u> protons... so it must have <u>seven</u> electrons.

2) Follow the 'Electron Shell Rules' above. The <u>first</u> shell can only take 2 electrons and the <u>second</u> shell can take a <u>maximum</u> of 8 electrons.

3) So the electron configuration for nitrogen <u>must</u> be <u>2, 5</u>. Easy peasy.

4) Now <u>you</u> try it for argon.

The periodic table has a big gap here where the transition metals fit in on row four.

H Hydrogen							He Helium
1 Proton no. = 1							2 Proton no. = 2
Li Lithium	Be Beryllium	B Boron	C Carbon	N Nitrogen	O Oxygen	F Fluorine	Ne Neon
2,1 Proton no. = 3	2,2 Proton no. = 4	2,3 Proton no. = 5	2,4 Proton no. = 6	2,5 Proton no. = 7	2,6 Proton no. = 8	2,7 Proton no. = 9	2,8 Proton no. = 10
Na Sodium	Mg Magnesium	Al Aluminium	Si Silicon	P Phosphorus	S Sulphur	Cl Chlorine	Ar Argon
2,8,1 Proton no. = 11	2,8,2 Proton no. = 12	2,8,3 Proton no. = 13	2,8,4 Proton no. = 14	2,8,5 Proton no. = 15	2,8,6 Proton no. = 16	2,8,7 Proton no. = 17	2,8,8 Proton no. = 18
K Potassium	Ca Calcium						
2,8,8,1 Proton no. = 19	2,8,8,2 Proton no. = 20						

<u>Answer...</u> To calculate the electron configuration of argon, <u>follow the rules</u>. It's got 18 protons, so it <u>must</u> have 18 electrons. The first shell must have <u>2</u> electrons, the second shell must have <u>8</u>, and so the third shell must have 8 as well. It's as easy as <u>2, 8, 8</u>.

One little duck and two fat ladies — 2, 8, 8...

You need to know enough about electron shells to draw out that <u>whole diagram</u> at the bottom of the page without looking at it. Obviously, you don't have to learn each element separately, just <u>learn the pattern</u>. Cover the page: using a periodic table, find the atom with the electron configuration 2, 8, 6.

Ionic Bonding

Ionic Bonding — Transfer of Electrons

In <u>ionic bonding</u>, atoms <u>lose or gain electrons</u> to form <u>charged particles</u> (called <u>ions</u>) which are then <u>strongly attracted</u> to one another (because of the attraction of opposite charges, + and –).

A Shell with Just One Electron is Well Keen to Get Rid...

<u>All</u> the atoms over at the <u>left-hand side</u> of the periodic table, e.g. <u>sodium, potassium, calcium</u> etc., have just <u>one or two electrons</u> in their outer shell. And they're <u>pretty keen to get shot of them</u>, because then they'll only have <u>full shells</u> left, which is how they <u>like</u> it. So given half a chance they do get rid, and that leaves the atom as an <u>ion</u> instead. Now ions aren't the kind of things that sit around quietly watching the world go by. They tend to <u>leap</u> at the first passing ion with an <u>opposite charge</u> and stick to it like glue.

A Nearly Full Shell is Well Keen to Get That Extra Electron...

On the <u>other side</u> of the periodic table, the elements in <u>Group 6</u> and <u>Group 7</u>, such as <u>oxygen</u> and <u>chlorine</u>, have outer shells which are <u>nearly full</u>. They're obviously pretty keen to <u>gain</u> that <u>extra one or two electrons</u> to fill the shell up. When they do of course they become <u>ions</u> (you know, not the kind of things to sit around) and before you know it, <u>pop</u>, they've latched onto the atom (ion) that gave up the electron a moment earlier. The reaction of sodium and chlorine is a <u>classic case</u>:

The <u>sodium</u> atom <u>gives up</u> its <u>outer electron</u> and becomes an Na^+ ion.

The <u>chlorine</u> atom <u>picks up</u> the <u>spare electron</u> and becomes a Cl^- ion.

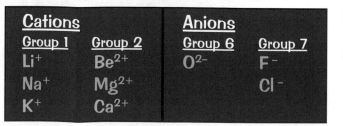

POP!

Groups 1 & 2 and 6 & 7 are the Most Likely to Form Ions

1) The elements that most readily form ions are those in Groups 1, 2, 6 and 7.

2) <u>Group 1 and 2 elements</u> are <u>metals</u> and they <u>lose</u> electrons to form <u>+ve ions</u> or <u>cations</u>.

3) <u>Group 6 and 7 elements</u> are <u>non-metals</u>. They <u>gain</u> electrons to form <u>–ve ions</u> or <u>anions</u>.

4) Make sure you know these easy ones:

Cations		Anions	
Group 1	Group 2	Group 6	Group 7
Li^+	Be^{2+}	O^{2-}	F^-
Na^+	Mg^{2+}		Cl^-
K^+	Ca^{2+}		

5) When any of these cations <u>react</u> with the anions, they form <u>ionic bonds</u>.

6) Only elements at <u>opposite sides</u> of the periodic table will form ionic bonds, e.g. Na and Cl, where one of them becomes a <u>cation</u> (+ve) and one becomes an <u>anion</u> (–ve).

Remember, the + and – charges we talk about, e.g. Na^+ for sodium, just tell you <u>what type of ion the atom WILL FORM</u> in a chemical reaction. In sodium <u>metal</u> there are <u>only neutral sodium atoms, Na</u>. The Na^+ ions <u>will only appear</u> if the sodium metal <u>reacts</u> with something like water or chlorine.

Any old ion, any old ion — any, any, any old ion...

Learn which atoms will form 1+, 1–, 2+ and 2– ions, and <u>why</u>. Then have a go at these:
1) What ions will each of these elements form?
   a) potassium, b) aluminium, c) beryllium, d) sulphur, e) fluorine (using a periodic table)

Answers on page 74.

Ionic Compounds

Ionic Compounds All Form in a Similar Way

Ionic compounds like this, with only two elements in, are called **BINARY SALTS**.

'Dot and cross' diagrams show what happens to the electrons in ionic bonds:

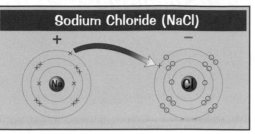

Sodium Chloride (NaCl)

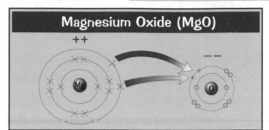

Magnesium Oxide (MgO)

The sodium atom gives up its outer electron, becoming an Na⁺ ion. The chlorine atom picks up the electron, becoming a Cl⁻ (chloride) ion.

The magnesium atom gives up its two outer electrons, becoming an Mg^{2+} ion. The oxygen atom picks up the electrons, becoming an O^{2-} (oxide) ion.

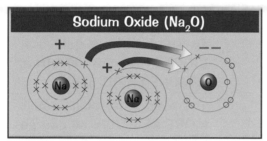

Sodium Oxide (Na₂O)

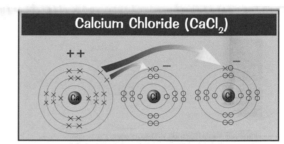

Calcium Chloride (CaCl₂)

Two sodium atoms give up their outer electrons, becoming two Na⁺ ions. The oxygen atom picks up the two electrons, becoming an O^{2-} ion.

The calcium atom gives up its two outer electrons, becoming a Ca^{2+} ion. The two chlorine atoms pick up one electron each, becoming two Cl⁻ (chloride) ions.

Notice that all the atoms end up with full outer shells as a result of this giving and taking of electrons.

Giant Ionic Structures Don't Melt Easily, but When They Do...

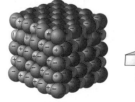

1) Ionic bonds always produce giant ionic structures.
2) The ions form a closely packed regular lattice arrangement.
3) There are very strong chemical bonds between all the ions.
4) A single crystal of salt is one giant ionic lattice, which is why salt crystals tend to be cuboid in shape.

1) They Have High Melting Points and Boiling Points

due to the very strong chemical bonds between all the ions in the giant structure.

2) They Dissolve to Form Solutions That Conduct Electricity

When dissolved the ions separate and are all free to move in the solution, so obviously they'll carry electric current. Dissolved lithium salts are used to make rechargeable batteries.

Dissolved in Water

Melted

3) They Conduct Electricity When Molten

When it melts, the ions are free to move and they'll carry electric current.

Giant ionic lattices — all over your chips...

Because they conduct electricity when they're dissolved in water, ionic compounds are used to make some types of battery. In the olden days, most batteries had actual liquid in, so they tended to leak all over the place. Now they've come up with a sort of paste that doesn't leak but still conducts. Clever.

C2 Topic 6 — In Your Element

Reactivity Trends

The reactivity of the elements in Groups 1 and 7 changes as you go down the group.
And it's all down to <u>electron configurations</u> again...

Reactivity Changes Down a Group Due to Shielding

1) As atoms get <u>bigger</u>, they have <u>more full shells</u> of electrons.
2) As you go down any group, each <u>new row</u> has <u>one more</u> full shell.
3) The number of <u>outer</u> electrons is the <u>same</u> for each element in a group.
4) However, going down the group, the outer shell of electrons becomes <u>increasingly far</u> from the nucleus.
5) You have to learn to say that the inner shells provide '<u>SHIELDING</u>'.
6) This means that the <u>outer shell electrons</u> get <u>shielded</u> from the <u>attraction</u> of the <u>+ve nucleus</u>.
   The <u>upshot</u> of all this is:

For Group 1 — the Alkali Metals

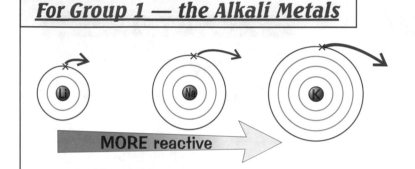

As Group 1 atoms get **BIGGER**, the outer electron is <u>**MORE EASILY LOST**</u>.

This makes the alkali metals <u>**MORE REACTIVE**</u> as you go <u>**DOWN**</u> the group.

MORE reactive

For Group 7 — the Halogens

As Group 7 atoms get **BIGGER**, the extra electron is <u>**HARDER TO GAIN**</u>.

This makes the halogens <u>**LESS REACTIVE**</u> as you go <u>**DOWN**</u> the group.

LESS reactive

The Noble Gases aren't Reactive At All

When atoms <u>react</u> with each other, they're trying to form <u>full outer shells</u>.

The <u>NOBLE GASES</u>, Group 0 elements, all have <u>FULL OUTER SHELLS</u> already — so they <u>DON'T REACT</u>.

Learn about electron shielding — keep up with the trends...

The <u>physical properties</u> of the alkali metals and the halogens also change as you go down the groups. As you go down the <u>halogens</u>, their boiling points increase and they get darker in colour. Going down the <u>alkali metals</u>, they get softer, denser and easier to melt. <u>Learn</u> the trends.

Metals

Metal Properties are All Due to the Sea of Free Electrons

1) Like ionic compounds, <u>metals</u> consist of a <u>giant structure</u>.

2) <u>Metallic bonds</u> involve the all-important '<u>free electrons</u>', which produce <u>all</u> the properties of metals.

3) These free electrons come from the <u>outer shell</u> of <u>every</u> metal atom in the structure.

Metal atoms

Free electrons

1) They're Good Conductors of Heat and Electricity

The <u>free electrons</u> carry both heat and electrical current through the material, so metals are good conductors of <u>heat and electricity</u>.

2) Most Metals are Malleable

Sheet of metal

Rollers

The layers of atoms in a metal can <u>slide</u> over each other, making metals <u>malleable</u> — they can be <u>hammered</u> or <u>rolled</u> into <u>flat sheets</u>.

3) They Generally Have High Melting and Boiling Points

Metallic bonds are <u>very strong</u>, so it takes a lot of <u>energy</u> to break them — you have to get the metal <u>pretty hot</u> (except for mercury, which is a bit weird), e.g. copper melts at 1085 °C and tungsten melts at 3422 °C.

4) Some Metals are Hard

The <u>hardness</u> of a metal is a measure of how easy it is to <u>dent</u> it. Some <u>transition metals</u> (like iron and tungsten) are hard, while the alkali metals are <u>quite soft</u>. The more malleable a metal is, the less hard it is — makes sense really.

Metals Can be Mixed Together to Make Alloys

You can <u>mix metals</u> with other things ('alloy' them) to change their <u>properties</u> — alloying usually makes metals <u>harder</u>.

1) <u>Steel</u> is an alloy of <u>iron</u> and about <u>1% carbon</u>. Steel is <u>stronger</u> and <u>less brittle</u> than iron.

2) <u>Bronze</u> is an alloy of <u>copper</u> and <u>tin</u>. It's <u>harder</u> than copper but still <u>easily shaped</u>.

3) <u>Copper</u> and <u>nickel</u> (75%:25%) are used to make <u>cupro-nickel</u> which is <u>hard</u> enough for <u>coins</u> (5p, 10p, 20p and 50p coins are cupro-nickel).

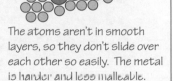

Pure metal	Alloy
Layers can slide over each other smoothly, so the metal is soft and malleable.	The atoms aren't in smooth layers, so they don't slide over each other so easily. The metal is harder and less malleable.

Metal fatigue? — yeah, we've all had enough of this page...

Some alloys have very different properties from their constituent metals. A good example is <u>nitinol</u> — an alloy of nickel and titanium. It's a metal, but when it's warm you can <u>bend it</u> and <u>twist it</u> like rubber. Nitinol has lots of applications — e.g. it's really handy for glasses frames.

Electrolysis and the Half-Equations

Electrolysis Means 'Splitting Up with Electricity'

1) Electrolysis is the breaking down of a substance using electricity.

2) It requires a liquid to conduct the electricity, called the electrolyte.

3) Electrolytes are usually ionic compounds that are either dissolved in water or molten.

4) In either case it's the free ions which conduct the electricity and make it work.

5) For an electrical circuit to be complete, there's got to be a flow of electrons. Electrons are taken away from ions at the positive anode and given to other ions at the negative cathode. As ions gain or lose electrons they become atoms or molecules.

NaCl dissolved

Molten NaCl

Electrolysis Removes Aluminium from Its Ore

1) The main ore of aluminium is bauxite, which contains aluminium oxide — Al_2O_3.

2) Molten aluminium oxide contains free ions — so it'll conduct electricity.

3) The positive Al^{3+} ions are attracted to the cathode where they pick up electrons and "zup", they turn into aluminium atoms. These then sink to the bottom.

4) The negative O^{2-} ions are attracted to the anode where they lose electrons. The oxygen atoms then react together to form O_2.

+ve ions are called **CATIONS** because they're attracted to the –ve cathode.

Aluminium is produced at the –ve cathode.

Cathode (-ve)   flow of electrons   flow of electrons   Anode (+ve)

molten aluminium oxide

molten aluminium metal

–ve ions are called **ANIONS** because they're attracted to the +ve anode.

Oxygen is produced at the +ve anode.

The Half-Equations — Make Sure the Electrons Balance

The main thing is to make sure the charges balance in each half-equation. For the above cell the half-equations are:

Cathode:	Al^{3+}	$+$ $3e^-$	$\rightarrow$	Al
Anode:	$2O^{2-}$	$\rightarrow$	O_2	$+$ $4e^-$

You have to be able to work out the products of the electrolysis of **ANY** molten binary salt. The salt splits up into its positive and negative ions. The positive ions pick up electrons at the cathode and the negative ions lose electrons at the anode:

e.g. molten K_2O would split into potassium (at the cathode) and oxygen (at the anode).

Cathode:	$4K^+$	$+$ $4e^-$	$\rightarrow$	$4K$
Anode:	$2O^{2-}$	$\rightarrow$	O_2	$+$ $4e^-$

Faster shopping at Tesco — use Electrolleys...

Electrolysis is fantastic for removing any unwanted hairs from your body. Great for women with moustaches, or men with hairy backs. And even better for the beauty clinic, as they'll get to charge a small fortune for the treatment. After all, all that electricity makes it a very expensive process...

Revision Summary for C2 Topic 6

These certainly aren't the easiest questions you're going to come across. That's because they test what you know without giving you any clues. At first you might think they're impossibly difficult. Eventually you'll realise that they simply test whether you've learnt the stuff or not.

If you're struggling to answer these then you need to do some serious learning.

1) Sketch the nuclear model of an atom.
   Give five details about the nucleus and five details about the electrons.
2) Draw a table showing the relative masses and charges of the three types of particle in an atom.
3) What do the mass number and atomic number represent?
4) Define the term isotope.
5)* The table below gives the masses and relative abundances of the isotopes of neon:

relative mass of isotope	relative abundance
20	91%
22	9%

   Calculate the relative atomic mass of neon. Give your answer to 2 decimal places.
6) What feature of atoms determines the order of the modern periodic table?
7) What are groups in the periodic table? Explain their significance in terms of electrons.
8) Describe how you would work out the electron configuration of an atom, given its atomic number.
   Find the electron configuration of potassium (using the periodic table at the front of the book).
9) Describe the process of ionic bonding.
10) List the main properties of ionic compounds.
11) State the trends in reactivity as you go down groups 1 and 7 of the periodic table.
    Explain these trends using the notion of 'shielding'.
12) Explain in terms of electrons why the noble gases are unreactive.
13) List five properties of metals and explain how metallic bonding causes these properties.
14) What is an alloy? Explain why alloys are often harder than the pure metal.
15) In electrolysis, why does the electrolyte have to be a liquid?
16) Describe what happens at the electrodes during the electrolysis of molten aluminium oxide.
    Write balanced half-equations for the reactions at the anode and cathode.
17)* Molten sodium oxide, Na_2O, is electrolysed to form two products.
    a) Name the two products and say which would form at which electrode.
    b) Write balanced half-equations for the reactions at the anode and cathode.

* Answers on page 74

C2 Topic 6 — In Your Element

Covalent Bonding

Some elements bond ionically (see Topic 6) but others form strong <u>covalent bonds</u>.

Covalent Bonds — Sharing Electrons

1) Sometimes atoms prefer to make <u>covalent bonds</u> by <u>sharing</u> electrons with other atoms.

2) This way <u>both</u> atoms feel that they have a <u>full outer shell</u>, and that makes them happy.

3) Each <u>covalent bond</u> provides one <u>extra</u> shared electron for each atom.

4) Each atom involved has to make <u>enough</u> covalent bonds to <u>fill up</u> its outer shell.

5) <u>Learn</u> these <u>four important examples</u>:

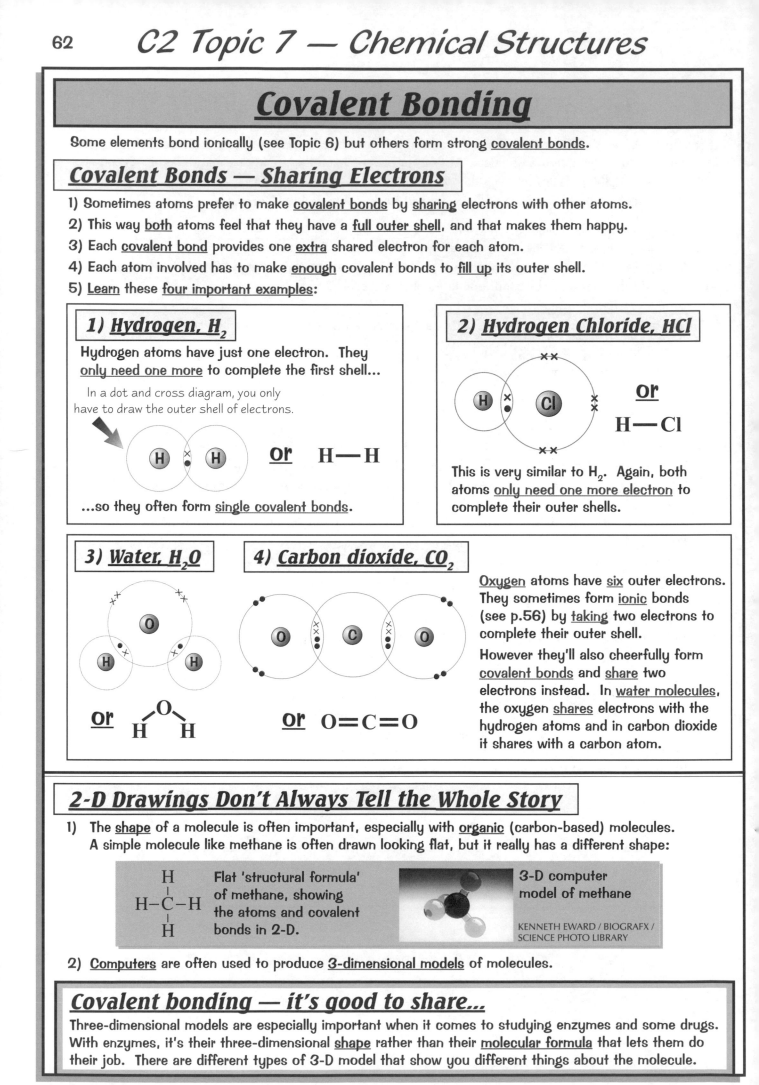

1) Hydrogen, H₂

Hydrogen atoms have just one electron. They <u>only need one more</u> to complete the first shell...

In a dot and cross diagram, you only have to draw the outer shell of electrons.

or   H—H

...so they often form <u>single covalent bonds</u>.

2) Hydrogen Chloride, HCl

or
H—Cl

This is very similar to H₂. Again, both atoms <u>only need one more electron</u> to complete their outer shells.

3) Water, H₂O

4) Carbon dioxide, CO₂

or $H \overset{O}{\diagdown} H$

or O=C=O

<u>Oxygen</u> atoms have <u>six</u> outer electrons. They sometimes form <u>ionic</u> bonds (see p.56) by <u>taking</u> two electrons to complete their outer shell.

However they'll also cheerfully form <u>covalent bonds</u> and <u>share</u> two electrons instead. In <u>water molecules</u>, the oxygen <u>shares</u> electrons with the hydrogen atoms and in carbon dioxide it shares with a carbon atom.

2-D Drawings Don't Always Tell the Whole Story

1) The <u>shape</u> of a molecule is often important, especially with <u>organic</u> (carbon-based) molecules. A simple molecule like methane is often drawn looking flat, but it really has a different shape:

$$H-\overset{\overset{\displaystyle H}{|}}{\underset{\underset{\displaystyle H}{|}}{C}}-H$$

Flat 'structural formula' of methane, showing the atoms and covalent bonds in 2-D.

3-D computer model of methane

KENNETH EWARD / BIOGRAFX / SCIENCE PHOTO LIBRARY

2) <u>Computers</u> are often used to produce <u>3-dimensional models</u> of molecules.

Covalent bonding — it's good to share...

Three-dimensional models are especially important when it comes to studying enzymes and some drugs. With enzymes, it's their three-dimensional <u>shape</u> rather than their <u>molecular formula</u> that lets them do their job. There are different types of 3-D model that show you different things about the molecule.

Molecular Substances: the Halogens

There are two kinds of covalent substance: <u>simple molecular</u> and <u>giant covalent</u> (next page).

Simple Molecular Substances

1) The atoms form <u>very strong</u> covalent bonds to form <u>small</u> molecules of two or more atoms.
2) By contrast, the forces of attraction <u>between</u> these molecules are <u>very weak</u>.
3) The result of these feeble <u>inter-molecular forces</u> is that the <u>melting</u> and <u>boiling points</u> are <u>very low</u>, because the molecules are <u>easily parted</u> from each other.
4) Most molecular substances are <u>gases or liquids</u> at room temperature.
5) Molecular substances <u>don't conduct electricity</u>, simply because there are <u>no ions</u>.
6) You can usually tell a molecular substance just from its <u>physical state</u>, which is always kinda 'mushy' — i.e. <u>liquid</u> or <u>gas</u> or an <u>easily-melted solid</u>.

Very weak inter-molecular forces

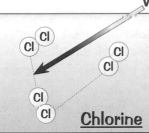 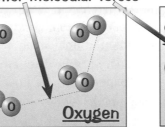 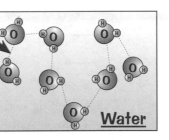

Chlorine   Oxygen   Water

The Halogens are All Simple Molecular

1) The <u>physical properties</u> of the <u>halogens</u> change down the group. Particularly, <u>melting point</u> and <u>boiling point</u> both <u>increase</u>.
2) This is because of the <u>strength</u> of the <u>inter-molecular forces</u>.

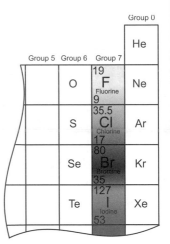

Group VII Elements	Atomic number	Colour	Physical state at room temperature	Melting point	Boiling point
Fluorine	9	yellow	gas	−220 °C	−188 °C
Chlorine	17	green	gas	−102 °C	−34 °C
Bromine	35	red-brown	liquid	−7 °C	59 °C
Iodine	53	dark grey	solid	114 °C	184 °C

3) The pattern in properties in the table can be explained because:
 • the halogens get <u>bigger</u> as you go <u>down the group</u>,
 • the <u>bigger</u> the halogen molecule, the <u>stronger</u> the <u>inter-molecular forces</u> of attraction,
 • the <u>stronger</u> the forces, the <u>more energy</u> it takes to <u>separate</u> the molecules, and so the higher their <u>melting points</u> and <u>boiling points</u>.
4) The little molecules of <u>fluorine</u> and <u>chlorine</u> have the weakest attraction to each other, so it takes very little energy to break them apart. That makes them <u>gases</u> at room temperature. The bigger molecules of <u>bromine</u> have stronger attractions, so it's a <u>liquid</u> at room temperature. Iodine's molecules are larger still. Its inter-molecular forces are the strongest of the four, and it's a <u>solid</u>.

Simple molecules? — not so sure about that...

So, simple molecules are held together by <u>weedy</u>, <u>pathetic</u> inter-molecular forces. But these forces get gradually less weedy as your molecules get bigger. That's why the halogens get more solid down the group. It's also why the alkanes (Topic 5, p.40) get less runny as they get bigger. Learn and enjoy.

Giant Covalent Structures: Carbon

Pure carbon usually forms <u>giant covalent structures</u>, rather than <u>molecules</u>.
<u>All</u> the atoms in the structure are bonded to each other by <u>strong covalent bonds</u>, so they have high melting and boiling points. The main examples are <u>diamond</u> and <u>graphite</u>.

Diamond is the Hardest Natural Substance

1) Pure diamond is <u>shiny</u>, <u>colourless</u> and <u>clear</u>. Ideal for jewellery.
2) Each carbon atom forms <u>four covalent bonds</u> in a <u>very rigid</u> giant covalent structure, which makes diamond <u>really hard</u>. This makes diamonds great as cutting tools.
3) There are lots of <u>strong covalent bonds</u>, so it's got <u>very high melting</u> and <u>boiling</u> points.
4) It <u>doesn't conduct electricity</u> because there are <u>no free electrons</u>.

Graphite is a Good Conductor of Electricity

1) Graphite is <u>black</u>, <u>opaque</u> and <u>lustrous</u> (kind of <u>shiny</u>).
2) Each carbon atom only forms <u>three covalent bonds</u>, creating <u>sheets of carbon atoms</u> which are free to <u>slide over each other</u>.
3) The layers are held together so loosely that they can be <u>rubbed off</u> onto paper — that's how a <u>pencil</u> works.
4) Graphite's got <u>high melting</u> and <u>boiling</u> points — the covalent bonds need <u>loads of energy</u> to break.
5) As only three out of each carbon's four outer electrons are used in bonds, there are lots of <u>spare electrons</u>. This makes graphite a <u>good conductor of electricity</u>.

Carbon Can Also Form Molecules Called Fullerenes

1) As well as giant structures, carbon can also form 'nanoparticle' molecules called <u>fullerenes</u>. These are molecules of <u>carbon</u>, shaped like <u>hollow balls</u> or <u>closed tubes</u>.
2) Each carbon atom forms <u>three</u> covalent bonds, leaving <u>free electrons</u> that <u>conduct</u> electricity.
3) The smallest fullerene is <u>buckminster fullerene</u>, which has <u>60</u> carbon atoms joined in a <u>ball</u> — its molecular formula is C_{60}.
4) Like a lot of scientific discoveries, C_{60} was discovered <u>by chance</u>. In the 1980s a group of scientists investigating how carbon chains are formed in stars fired <u>laser beams</u> at graphite discs. When they analysed the soot formed, they found that clusters of 60 carbon atoms were <u>surprisingly common</u>. These turned out to be the first 'sightings' of buckminster fullerene.

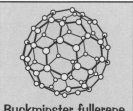
Buckminster fullerene

Fullerenes can be joined together to form <u>nanotubes</u> — teeny tiny hollow carbon tubes, a few nanometres across:

a) All those covalent bonds make carbon nanotubes <u>very strong</u> for their mass. They can be used to reinforce graphite in tennis rackets and to make stronger, lighter building materials — these materials are called <u>nanocomposites</u>.
b) Nanotubes <u>conduct</u> electricity, so they can be used in tiny <u>electric circuits</u> for computer chips.
c) They have a <u>huge surface area</u>, so they could help make great industrial <u>catalysts</u> (see page 70) — individual catalyst molecules could be attached to carbon nanotubes.

Carbon is a girl's best friend...

Nanoparticles can be made by <u>molecular engineering</u> — either by building a product <u>atom by atom</u>, placing each atom exactly where you want it, or by starting with a bigger structure and taking bits off it.

Treatment and Homeopathy

I bet you're wondering what on earth homeopathy's got to do with chemical structures.
Yeh — well, you're not the only one...

Conventional Medicines Go Through Rigorous Testing

1) <u>Chemical-based medicines</u> have to go through years of <u>testing</u> before they can be sold (see p.45).

2) The final stage of this testing involves giving <u>some patients</u> a tablet containing the drug and <u>others</u> an <u>identical looking</u> tablet that doesn't contain the drug — a <u>placebo</u>.

3) Some people in the placebo '<u>control group</u>' will get better <u>naturally</u> and others will feel better just because they <u>think</u> they're being treated (called the 'placebo effect').

4) <u>Huge samples</u> are used for the tests, and it's often only possible to say if a drug is working or not by carefully comparing <u>ALL</u> the results. Only if a drug is shown scientifically to be useful (and to not have too many dangerous side effects) will a company be granted a licence to sell it.

5) In the exam, you might have to decide (using information they give you) whether a drug is effective or not. The <u>main things</u> to look out for are:

- Did the people taking the drug <u>get better</u>? (Bit of an obvious one, there.)
- Was the sample <u>big enough</u>? (A study of 1000 people is probably more reliable than one using 50.)
- Did the study use a suitable <u>control group</u>?
- How did the results from the control group <u>compare</u> with the results from the group actually taking the drug? If <u>both groups</u> got better, the test proves <u>nothing</u>.

Some Alternative Remedies aren't Chemical-Based

1) <u>Homeopathic remedies</u> contain <u>highly diluted</u> doses of natural substances that in their full-strength dose would produce the <u>symptoms of illness</u> in a healthy person.

2) The theory is that a patient's <u>own immune system</u> responds to this substance and fights the disease.

3) Remedies are made by extracting the <u>active ingredient</u> from a plant, animal or mineral, dissolving it in alcohol and then progressively <u>diluting</u> the mixture with water. A <u>shaking process</u> between each dilution is said to transfer the <u>powers</u> of the ingredients to the water.

4) The makers claim the remedies become <u>more powerful</u> the <u>more dilute</u> they are. Many doctors and scientists find it <u>difficult to accept</u> this, since it's <u>contrary</u> to conventional science (see p.67).

5) Homeopathic remedies can be <u>so dilute</u> that they are unlikely to contain <u>any</u> molecules of the active ingredient at all. The makers say that the shaking process leaves a '<u>footprint</u>' of the original active ingredient in the water. There is no <u>scientific evidence</u> for this, though.

6) Homeopathic remedies don't have to go through the same <u>testing</u> as conventional medicines — the amounts of active ingredients are so low they're considered <u>harmless</u> — so there have been <u>very few</u> large-scale trials. A few small trials have suggested that they <u>do work</u>, while <u>others</u> suggest they <u>don't</u>. A recent study combining <u>all the data</u> gathered so far suggests that they work <u>no better</u> than a <u>placebo</u>, but many people still believe in the power of homeopathy.

Other non-conventional treatments include <u>crystals</u> and the wearing of <u>copper</u> and <u>magnetic bracelets</u>.

Some people believe that <u>crystals</u> have <u>healing properties</u>. Some think that just <u>wearing</u> or <u>holding</u> the correct crystal is enough. Other people claim to be able to use the power of crystals to <u>heal others</u> by holding crystals over the affected parts of the body.

<u>Copper</u> and, more recently, <u>magnetic bracelets</u> are said to help a variety of painful ailments including <u>arthritis</u> and <u>rheumatism</u>.

Proven or not, homeopathy is big business...

There's no shortage of people who believe that homeopathy, crystals and copper have cured them when conventional medicine couldn't. But there's <u>no scientific evidence</u> that these treatments work.

Revision Summary for C2 Topic 7

That was short and sweet... well, short anyway.

And now here are some more questions for you to get your teeth into. Have a go at them. If there are any you can't do, go back to the section and do a bit more learning, then try again. It's not fun, but it's the best way to make sure you know everything. Hop to it.

1) What is covalent bonding?

2) Sketch dot and cross diagrams showing the bonding in molecules of:
   a) hydrogen, b) hydrogen chloride, c) water, d) carbon dioxide.

3) Why are two-dimensional representations of molecules (e.g. dot and cross diagrams) sometimes not very useful?

4) Give three physical properties of simple molecular substances.

5) Explain how the bonding in simple molecular substances causes the properties you listed for Q4.

6) Describe the trend in boiling point as you go down Group 7.
   Explain this trend in terms of inter-molecular forces.

7) Describe and explain the differences between the physical properties of simple molecular substances and giant covalent substances.

8) Explain, in terms of their bonding, why graphite conducts electricity but diamond doesn't.

9) What are fullerenes?

10) Describe briefly how buckminster fullerene was discovered.

11)* What property of carbon nanotubes makes them useful for graphite tennis rackets? Why might it be better to use nanotubes than, e.g., steel in building materials?

12)* Carbon nanotubes can conduct electricity. Suggest an advantage of using nanotubes rather than conventional wires in computer circuits.

13) The table below shows the results from a clinical trial of a drug. The test group were given tablets containing the active ingredient. The control group were given identical-looking placebos.

	Change in condition after treatment		
	No change	Some improvement	Full recovery
Test group	72	52	176
Control group	192	86	22

a)* How many patients were involved in the trial altogether?

b)* Did this trial suggest that the drug is effective? Explain your answer as fully as you can.

c) Suggest why some people in the control group improved or made a full recovery.

14) Based on your knowledge of homeopathic medicine, suggest why scientists find it difficult to believe in its effectiveness.

* Answers on page 74

Rates of Reaction

Reactions Can Go at All Sorts of Different Rates

1) One of the <u>slowest</u> is the <u>rusting</u> of iron (it's not slow enough though — what about my little MGB).

2) An example of a <u>moderate speed</u> reaction is a <u>metal</u> (like magnesium) reacting with <u>acid</u> to produce a gentle stream of <u>bubbles</u>.

3) A <u>really fast</u> reaction is an <u>explosion</u>, where it's all over in a <u>fraction</u> of a second.

The Rate of a Reaction Depends on Four Things:

1) <u>Temperature</u>
2) <u>Concentration</u> — (or <u>pressure</u> for gases)
3) <u>Catalyst</u>
4) <u>Size of particles</u> — (or <u>surface area</u>)

LEARN THEM!

Typical Graphs for Rate of Reaction

The plot below shows how the speed of a particular reaction varies under <u>different conditions</u>. The quickest reaction is shown by the line that becomes <u>flat</u> in the <u>least</u> time. The quickest reaction will also start with the steepest slope, and the slowest reaction with the shallowest slope.

1) <u>Graph 1</u> represents the original <u>fairly slow</u> reaction. The graph is not too steep.

2) <u>Graphs 2 and 3</u> represent the reaction taking place <u>quicker</u> but with the <u>same initial amounts</u>. The slope of the graphs gets steeper.

3) The <u>increased rate</u> could be due to <u>any</u> of these:

   a) increase in <u>temperature</u>
   b) increase in <u>concentration</u> (or pressure)
   c) <u>catalyst</u> added
   d) solid reactant crushed up into <u>smaller bits</u>.

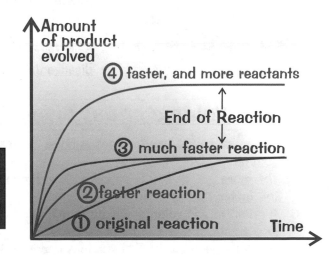

4) <u>Graph 4</u> shows <u>more product</u> as well as a <u>faster reaction</u>. This can <u>only</u> happen if <u>more reactant(s)</u> are added at the start. <u>Graphs 1, 2 and 3</u> all converge at the same level, showing that they all produce the same amount of product, although they take <u>different</u> times to get there.

How to get a fast, furious reaction — crack a wee joke...

<u>Industrial</u> reactions generally use a <u>catalyst</u> and are done at <u>high temperature and pressure</u>. Time is money, so the faster an industrial reaction goes the better... but only <u>up to a point</u>. Chemical plants are quite expensive to rebuild if they get blown into lots and lots of teeny tiny pieces.

Measuring Rates of Reaction

Three Ways to Measure the Speed of a Reaction

The <u>speed of a reaction</u> can be observed <u>either</u> by how quickly the reactants are used up or how quickly the products are formed. It's usually a lot easier to measure <u>products forming</u>.

The rate of reaction can be calculated using the following equation:

$$\text{Rate of Reaction} = \frac{\text{Amount of reactant used or amount of product formed}}{\text{Time}}$$

There are different ways that the speed of a reaction can be <u>measured</u>. Learn these three:

1) Precipitation

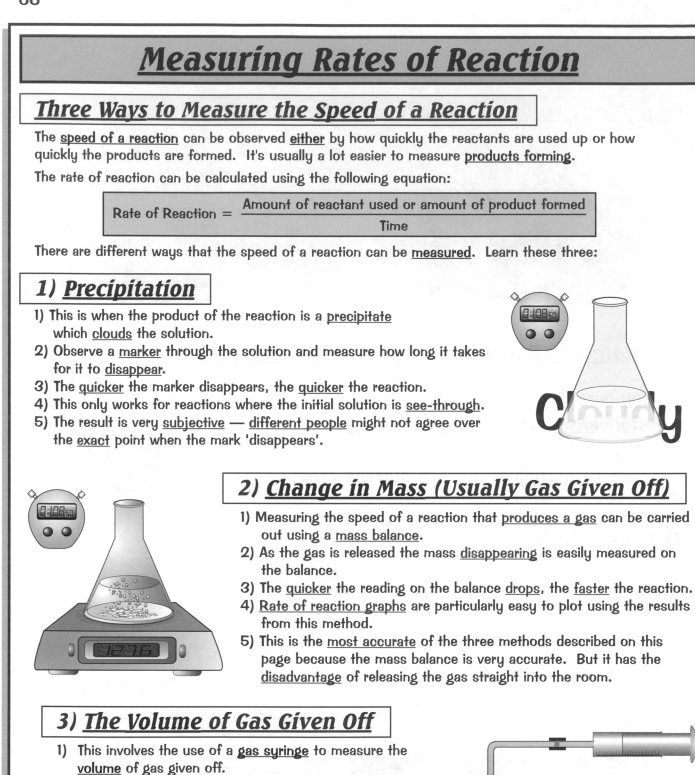

1) This is when the product of the reaction is a <u>precipitate</u> which <u>clouds</u> the solution.
2) Observe a <u>marker</u> through the solution and measure how long it takes for it to <u>disappear</u>.
3) The <u>quicker</u> the marker disappears, the <u>quicker</u> the reaction.
4) This only works for reactions where the initial solution is <u>see-through</u>.
5) The result is very <u>subjective</u> — <u>different people</u> might not agree over the <u>exact</u> point when the mark 'disappears'.

2) Change in Mass (Usually Gas Given Off)

1) Measuring the speed of a reaction that <u>produces a gas</u> can be carried out using a <u>mass balance</u>.
2) As the gas is released the mass <u>disappearing</u> is easily measured on the balance.
3) The <u>quicker</u> the reading on the balance <u>drops</u>, the <u>faster</u> the reaction.
4) <u>Rate of reaction graphs</u> are particularly easy to plot using the results from this method.
5) This is the <u>most accurate</u> of the three methods described on this page because the mass balance is very accurate. But it has the <u>disadvantage</u> of releasing the gas straight into the room.

3) The Volume of Gas Given Off

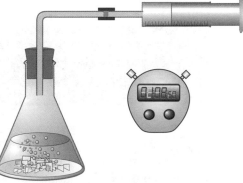

1) This involves the use of a <u>gas syringe</u> to measure the <u>volume</u> of gas given off.
2) The <u>more</u> gas given off during a given <u>time interval</u>, the <u>faster</u> the reaction.
3) A graph of <u>gas volume</u> against <u>time</u> could be plotted to give a rate of reaction graph.
4) Gas syringes usually give volumes accurate to the <u>nearest</u> <u>cm³</u>, so they're quite accurate. You have to be quite careful though — if the reaction is too <u>vigorous</u>, you can easily blow the plunger out of the end of the syringe!

OK have you got your stopwatch ready *BANG!* — oh...

Each method has its <u>pros and cons</u>. The mass balance method is only accurate as long as the flask isn't too hot, otherwise you lose mass by evaporation as well as by the reaction. The first method isn't very accurate, but if you're not producing a gas you can't use either of the other two. Ah well.

Collision Theory

Reaction rates are explained perfectly by <u>collision theory</u>. It's really simple.
It just says that <u>the rate of a reaction</u> simply depends on <u>how often</u> and <u>how hard</u>
the reacting particles <u>collide</u> with each other. The basic idea is that particles have to
<u>collide</u> in order to <u>react</u>, and they have to collide <u>hard enough</u> (with enough energy).

More Collisions Increases the Rate of Reaction

All four methods of increasing the <u>rate of reactions</u> can be <u>explained</u> in terms of increasing the
<u>number of successful collisions</u> between the reacting particles:

1) HIGHER TEMPERATURE increases collisions

When the <u>temperature is increased</u> the particles all <u>move quicker</u>.
If they're moving quicker, they're going to have <u>more collisions</u>.

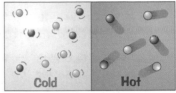

Cold   Hot

2) HIGHER CONCENTRATION (or PRESSURE) increases collisions

If a solution is made more <u>concentrated</u> it means there are more
particles of <u>reactant</u> knocking about <u>between the water molecules</u>,
which makes collisions between the <u>important</u> particles <u>more likely</u>.
In a <u>gas</u>, increasing the <u>pressure</u> means the particles are <u>more</u>
<u>squashed up</u> together so there are going to be <u>more collisions</u>.

Low Concentration   High Concentration
(Low Pressure)   (High Pressure)

3) LARGER SURFACE AREA increases collisions

If one of the reactants is a <u>solid</u> then <u>breaking it up</u> into
<u>smaller</u> pieces will <u>increase its surface area</u>. This means
the particles around it in the solution will have <u>more area</u>
<u>to work on</u>, so there'll be <u>more useful collisions</u>.

4) CATALYSTS increase the number of SUCCESSFUL collisions

A <u>solid catalyst</u> works by giving the <u>reacting particles</u> a
<u>surface</u> to <u>stick to</u>. They increase the number of
<u>SUCCESSFUL</u> collisions by lowering the <u>activation energy</u>
(see next page).

Surface of catalyst

Faster Collisions Increase the Rate of Reaction

<u>Higher temperature</u> also increases the <u>energy</u> of the collisions, because it makes all the particles <u>move faster</u>.

Faster collisions are ONLY caused by increasing the temperature.

Reactions <u>only happen</u> if the particles collide with <u>enough energy</u>.
At a <u>higher temperature</u> there will be <u>more particles</u>
colliding with <u>enough energy</u> to make the reaction happen.
The <u>minimum energy</u> required is known as the <u>activation energy</u>,
and it's needed to <u>break the initial bonds</u>.

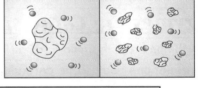

Cool Atoms   Hot Atoms

Collision theory — that lamppost ran into me...

Once you've learnt everything off this page, the rates of reaction stuff should start making <u>a lot more</u>
<u>sense</u> to you. The concept's fairly simple — the <u>more often</u> particles bump into each other, and the
<u>harder</u> they hit when they do, the <u>faster</u> the reaction happens.

Catalysts

Many reactions can be <u>speeded up</u> by adding a <u>catalyst</u>.

> A <u>catalyst</u> is a substance which <u>changes</u> the speed of a reaction,
> without being <u>changed</u> or <u>used up</u> in the reaction.

1) *Catalysts Lower the Activation Energy*

1) The <u>activation energy</u> is the <u>minimum</u> amount of energy needed for a reaction to happen.

2) It's a bit like having to <u>climb up</u> one side of a hill before you can ski/snowboard/sledge/fall down the <u>other side</u>.

3) Catalysts <u>lower</u> the <u>activation energy</u> of reactions, making it <u>easier</u> for them to happen.

4) This means a <u>lower temperature</u> can be used.

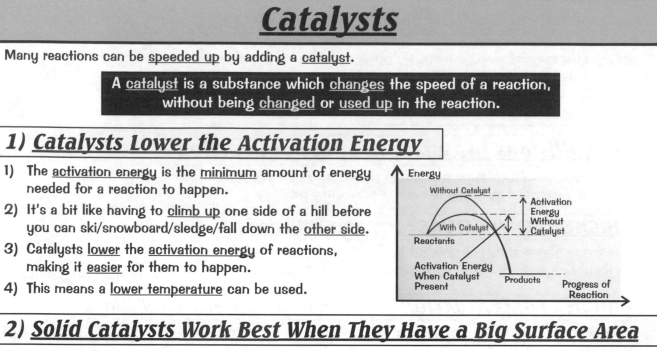

2) *Solid Catalysts Work Best When They Have a Big Surface Area*

1) Catalysts are usually used as a <u>powder</u> or <u>pellets</u> or a <u>fine gauze</u>.

2) This gives them <u>a very large surface area</u> to enable the reacting particles to <u>meet up</u> and do the business.

Catalyst Powder   Catalyst Pellets   Catalyst Gauzes

3) <u>Transition metals</u> are common catalysts in <u>industrial</u> reactions, e.g. <u>iron</u> in the <u>Haber process</u> (p.73).

3) *Enzymes are Catalysts Produced by Living Things*

1) <u>Living things</u> have thousands of different <u>chemical reactions</u> going on inside them all the time.

2) These reactions need to be <u>carefully controlled</u> — to get the <u>right</u> amounts of substances.

3) You can usually make a reaction happen more quickly by <u>raising the temperature</u>. This would speed up the useful reactions but also the unwanted ones too... not good. There's also a <u>limit</u> to how far you can raise the temperature inside a living creature before its <u>cells</u> start getting <u>damaged</u>.

4) So... living things produce <u>enzymes</u> which act as <u>biological catalysts</u>. Enzymes reduce the need for high temperatures and we <u>only</u> have enzymes to speed up the <u>useful chemical reactions</u> in the body.

5) Enzymes are <u>proteins</u>. Each enzyme is folded into a <u>unique shape</u> that it needs to do its job.

Enzymes Need the Right Temperature and pH

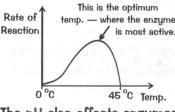

1) In an enzyme-catalysed reaction, a higher temperature <u>increases</u> the rate at first. But if it gets <u>too hot</u>, some of the <u>bonds</u> in the enzyme <u>break</u>. This destroys the enzyme's <u>special shape</u> and so it won't work any more. It's said to be <u>denatured</u>.

2) Enzymes in the <u>human body</u> normally work best at around <u>37 °C</u>.

3) The <u>pH</u> also affects enzymes. If it's too high or too low, it changes the shape and <u>denatures</u> the enzyme.

4) All enzymes have an <u>optimum pH</u> that they work best at. It's often <u>neutral</u> <u>pH 7</u>, but <u>not always</u> — e.g. pepsin (a stomach enzyme) works best at <u>pH 2</u>.

Catalysts are like great jokes — they can be used over and over...

And they're not only used in <u>industry</u>... every useful chemical reaction in the human body is catalysed by a <u>biological catalyst</u> (an enzyme). If the reactions in the body were just left to their own devices, they'd take so long to happen, we couldn't exist. Quite handy then, these catalysts.

Energy Transfer in Reactions

In a chemical reaction, <u>energy</u> is usually <u>transferred</u> to or from the <u>surroundings</u>, and it's all about making and breaking bonds.

Energy Must Always be Supplied to Break Bonds

1) During a chemical reaction, <u>old bonds are broken</u> and <u>new bonds are formed</u>.
2) Energy must be <u>supplied</u> to break <u>existing bonds</u> — so bond breaking is an <u>endothermic</u> process.
3) Energy is <u>released</u> when new bonds are <u>formed</u> — so bond formation is an <u>exothermic</u> process.

BOND BREAKING - <u>ENDOTHERMIC</u>

Na Cl → Na + Cl
Strong Bond — Energy Supplied — Bond Broken

BOND FORMING - <u>EXOTHERMIC</u>

Mg + O → Mg O + Energy Released
Strong Bond Formed

In an Exothermic Reaction, Energy is Given Out

1) In an <u>EXOTHERMIC</u> reaction, the energy <u>released</u> in bond formation is <u>greater</u> than the energy used in <u>breaking</u> old bonds.

An <u>EXOTHERMIC reaction</u> is one which <u>GIVES OUT ENERGY</u> to the surroundings, usually in the form of <u>heat</u> and usually shown by a <u>RISE IN TEMPERATURE</u>.

2) <u>Burning fuels</u> (<u>COMBUSTION</u>) gives out a lot of heat — it's very exothermic. That's because making new bonds in the products (water and carbon dioxide) gives out <u>much more energy</u> than it takes to break the bonds in the fuel.
3) <u>Neutralisation reactions</u> (acid + alkali) are also exothermic.

ACID
Don't do it like this!!
ALKALI

In an Endothermic Reaction, Energy is Taken In

1) In an <u>ENDOTHERMIC</u> reaction, the energy <u>required</u> to break old bonds is <u>greater</u> than the energy <u>released</u> when <u>new bonds</u> are formed.

An <u>ENDOTHERMIC reaction</u> is one which <u>TAKES IN ENERGY</u> from the surroundings, usually in the form of <u>heat</u> and usually shown by a <u>FALL IN TEMPERATURE</u>.

2) Endothermic reactions are much <u>less common</u>. <u>Thermal decompositions</u> are a good example:

<u>THERMAL DECOMPOSITION OF CALCIUM CARBONATE</u>:
Heat must be supplied to break some of the bonds and make the compound <u>decompose</u> to form quicklime:

$$CaCO_3 \rightarrow CaO + CO_2$$

<u>A lot of heat energy</u> is needed to make this happen. In fact the calcium carbonate has to be <u>heated in a kiln</u> and kept at about <u>800 °C</u>. It takes almost <u>18 000 kJ</u> of heat to make <u>10 kg</u> of calcium carbonate decompose. That's pretty endothermic I'd say.

Right, so burning gives out heat — really...

This whole energy transfer thing is a fairly simple idea — don't be put off by the long words. Remember, "exo-" = <u>exit</u>, "-thermic" = <u>heat</u>, so an exothermic reaction is one that <u>gives out</u> heat. And "endo-" = erm... the other one. Okay, so there's no easy way to remember that one. Tough.

Reversible Reactions

A <u>reversible reaction</u> is one where the <u>products</u> of the reaction can react with each other and <u>convert back</u> to the original reactants. In other words, <u>it can go both ways</u>.

> A <u>reversible reaction</u> is one where the <u>products</u> of the reaction can <u>themselves react</u> to produce the <u>original reactants</u>.
>
> A + B $\rightleftharpoons$ C + D
>
> This is the symbol for a reversible reaction.

Reversible Reactions Will Reach Dynamic Equilibrium

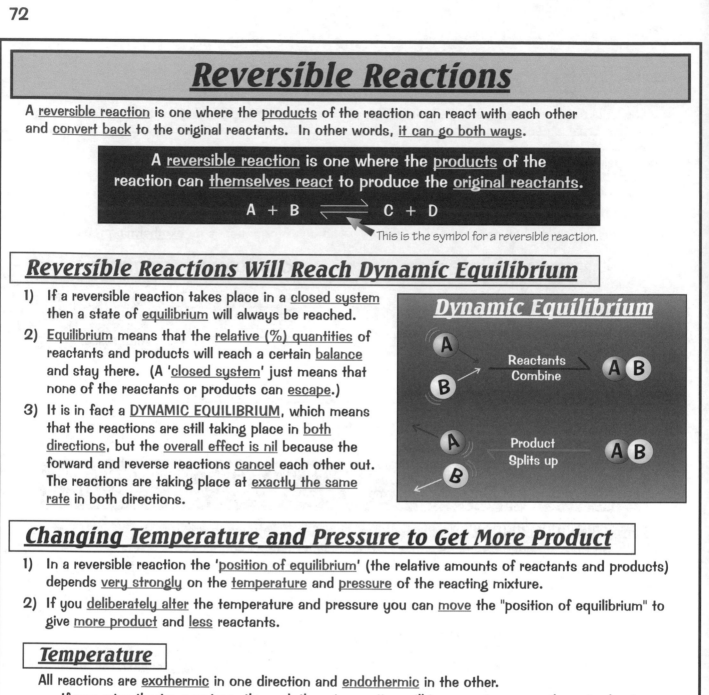

Dynamic Equilibrium

Reactants Combine

Product Splits up

1) If a reversible reaction takes place in a <u>closed system</u> then a state of <u>equilibrium</u> will always be reached.

2) <u>Equilibrium</u> means that the <u>relative (%) quantities</u> of reactants and products will reach a certain <u>balance</u> and stay there. (A '<u>closed system</u>' just means that none of the reactants or products can <u>escape</u>.)

3) It is in fact a <u>DYNAMIC EQUILIBRIUM</u>, which means that the reactions are still taking place in <u>both directions</u>, but the <u>overall effect is nil</u> because the forward and reverse reactions <u>cancel</u> each other out. The reactions are taking place at <u>exactly the same rate</u> in both directions.

Changing Temperature and Pressure to Get More Product

1) In a reversible reaction the '<u>position of equilibrium</u>' (the relative amounts of reactants and products) depends <u>very strongly</u> on the <u>temperature</u> and <u>pressure</u> of the reacting mixture.

2) If you <u>deliberately alter</u> the temperature and pressure you can <u>move</u> the "position of equilibrium" to give <u>more product</u> and <u>less</u> reactants.

Temperature

All reactions are <u>exothermic</u> in one direction and <u>endothermic</u> in the other.
  If you <u>raise</u> the <u>temperature</u>, the <u>endothermic</u> reaction will increase to <u>use up</u> the extra heat.
  If you <u>reduce</u> the <u>temperature</u>, the <u>exothermic</u> reaction will increase to <u>give out</u> more heat.

Pressure

Many reactions have a <u>greater volume</u> on one side, either of <u>products</u> or <u>reactants</u> (greater volume means there are more molecules and less volume means there are fewer molecules).
  If you <u>raise</u> the <u>pressure</u> it will encourage the reaction which produces <u>less volume</u>.
  If you <u>lower</u> the <u>pressure</u> it will encourage the reaction which produces <u>more volume</u>.

  <u>Adding a CATALYST doesn't change the equilibrium position:</u>
  1) Catalysts speed up <u>both</u> the <u>forward</u> and <u>backward</u> reactions by the <u>same amount</u>.
  2) So, adding a catalyst means the reaction reaches equilibrium <u>quicker</u>, but you end up with the <u>same amount</u> of product as you would without the catalyst.

Remember — catalysts DON'T affect the equilibrium position...

Changing the temperature <u>always</u> changes the equilibrium position, but that's not true of pressure. If your reaction has the same number of molecules on each side of the equation, changing the pressure won't make any difference at all to the equilibrium position (it still affects the <u>rate</u> of reaction though).

The Haber Process

Nitrogen and Hydrogen are Needed to Make Ammonia

$$N_{2(g)} + 3H_{2(g)} \rightleftharpoons 2NH_{3(g)} \text{ (+ heat)}$$

1) The nitrogen is obtained easily from the air, which is 78% nitrogen (and 21% oxygen).
2) The hydrogen comes from natural gas or from other sources like crude oil.
3) Because the reaction is reversible — it occurs in both directions — not all of the nitrogen and hydrogen will convert to ammonia. The reaction reaches a dynamic equilibrium.

Industrial conditions: Pressure: 200 atmospheres; Temperature: 450 °C; Catalyst: Iron

The Reaction is Reversible, So There's a Compromise to be Made:

1) Higher pressures favour the forward reaction (since there are four molecules of gas on the left-hand side for every two molecules on the right).
2) So the pressure is set as high as possible to give the best % yield, without making the plant too expensive to build. Hence the 200 atmospheres operating pressure.
3) The forward reaction is exothermic, which means that increasing the temperature will actually move the equilibrium the wrong way — away from ammonia and towards N_2 and H_2. So the yield of ammonia would be greater at lower temperatures.
4) The trouble is, lower temperatures mean a slower rate of reaction. So what they do is increase the temperature anyway, to get a much faster rate of reaction.
5) The 450 °C is a compromise between maximum yield and speed of reaction. It's better to wait just 20 seconds for a 10% yield than to have to wait 60 seconds for a 20% yield.

H₂ and N₂ mixed in 3:1 ratio
H₂
N₂
Reaction vessel
Trays of iron catalyst
450°C 200 atm
Unused N₂ and H₂ is recycled
Condenser
Liquid Ammonia

6) The ammonia is formed as a gas, but as it cools in the condenser it liquefies and is removed. The unused hydrogen, H_2, and nitrogen, N_2, are recycled, so nothing is wasted.
7) The iron catalyst makes the reaction go faster, but doesn't affect the % yield.

Ammonia is Used to Make Ammonium Nitrate Fertiliser

1) If you react ammonia with nitric acid, you get ammonium nitrate. Ammonium nitrate is an especially good fertiliser because it has nitrogen from two sources, the ammonia and the nitric acid. Kind of a double dose. Plants need nitrogen to make proteins.
2) Ammonium nitrate is a much more effective fertiliser than organic alternatives (e.g. pig poo), so it helps farmers produce crops from land that otherwise wouldn't have been fertile enough.
3) There are serious problems with artificial fertilisers, though:
   a) If nitrate fertilisers wash into streams they can set off a cycle of mega-growth, mega-death and mega-decay. It's called eutrophication (see Topic 3, page 21 for more details).
   b) If too many nitrates get into drinking water it can cause health problems, especially for young babies. Nitrates prevent the blood from carrying oxygen properly and children can die from it.
4) To help avoid these problems it's important that artificial nitrate fertilisers are applied carefully by all farmers — they must take care not to apply too much, and not to apply them if it's likely to rain soon.

You need to learn this stuff — go on, Haber go at it...

The trickiest bit is remembering that the temperature is raised not for a better equilibrium, but for speed.

Revision Summary for C2 Topic 8

Well, I don't think that was too bad, was it. Four things affect the rate of reactions, there are loads of ways to measure reaction rates and it's all explained by collision theory. Reactions can be endothermic or exothermic, and quite a few of them are reversible. Easy. Ahem.

Well here are some more of those nice questions that you enjoy so much. If there are any you can't answer, go back to the appropriate page, do a bit more learning, then try again.

1) What are the four factors that affect the rate of a reaction?

2) Describe three different ways of measuring the rate of a reaction. List one advantage and one disadvantage of each method.

3) A student carries out an experiment to measure the effect of surface area on the reaction between marble and hydrochloric acid. He measures the amount of gas given off at regular intervals.
   a) What factors must he keep constant for it to be a fair test?
   b)* He uses four samples for his experiment:
      Sample A – 10 g of powdered marble
      Sample B – 10 g of small marble chips
      Sample C – 10 g of large marble chips
      Sample D – 5 g of powdered marble
   Sketch a typical set of graphs for this experiment.

4) A catalyst can increase the rate of a reaction. Explain how each of the three other factors which affect reaction rates increase the number of collisions between particles.

5) What is the other aspect of collision theory which determines the rate of reaction?

6) Which is the only physical factor which affects this other aspect of collision theory?

7) What is the definition of a catalyst? What does a catalyst do to the activation energy of a reaction?

8) What is an exothermic reaction? Give two examples.

9) The reaction to split ammonium chloride into ammonia and hydrogen chloride is endothermic. What can you say for certain about the reverse reaction?

10) What is a reversible reaction? Explain what is meant by a dynamic equilibrium.

11) How does changing the temperature and pressure of a reversible reaction alter the equilibrium position?

12) How does this influence the choice of pressure for the Haber process?

13) What determines the choice of operating temperature for the Haber process?

14) What effect does the iron catalyst have on the reaction between nitrogen and hydrogen?

* Answer below

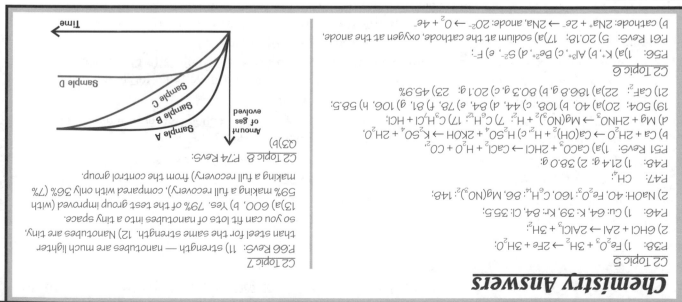

Chemistry Answers

C2 Topic 5
P38: 1) $Fe_2O_3 + 3H_2 \rightarrow 2Fe + 3H_2O$.

P46: 1) Cu: 64, K: 39, Kr: 84, Cl: 35.5.
2) $6HCl + 2Al \rightarrow 2AlCl_3 + 3H_2$.

P47: CH_4.

P48: 1) 21.4 g. 2) 38.0 g.

2) NaOH: 40, Fe_2O_3: 160, C_4H_{10}: 86, $Mg(NO_3)_2$: 148.

P51 Revs: 1)a) $CaCO_3 + 2HCl \rightarrow CaCl_2 + H_2O + CO_2$,
b) $Ca + 2H_2O \rightarrow Ca(OH)_2 + H_2$, c) $H_2SO_4 + 2KOH \rightarrow K_2SO_4 + 2H_2O$,
d) $Mg + 2HNO_3 \rightarrow Mg(NO_3)_2 + H_2$; 7) C_6H_{12}; 17) $C_3H_7Cl + HCl$.
19) 504; 20)a) 40, b) 108, c) 44, d) 84, e) 78, f) 81, g) 106, h) 58.5;
21) CaF_2; 22)a) 186.8 g, b) 80.3 g, c) 20.1 g; 23) 45.9%

C2 Topic 6
P56: 1)a) K^+, b) Al^{3+}, c) Be^{2+}, d) S^{2-}, e) F^-;
P61 Revs: 5) 20:18. 17)a) sodium at the cathode, oxygen at the anode,
b) cathode: $2Na^+ + 2e^- \rightarrow 2Na$, anode: $2O^{2-} \rightarrow O_2 + 4e^-$.

C2 Topic 7
P66 Revs: 11) strength — nanotubes are much lighter than steel for the same strength. 12) Nanotubes are tiny, so you can fit lots of nanotubes into a tiny space.
13)a) 600. b) Yes. 79% of the test group improved (with making a full recovery), compared with only 36% (7% 59% making a full recovery) from the control group.

C2 Topic 8 P74 Revs:
Q3)b)

Speed and Velocity

Speed and Velocity are Both: HOW FAST YOU'RE GOING

Speed and velocity are both measured in <u>m/s</u> (or km/h or mph). They both simply say <u>how fast</u> you're going, but there's <u>a subtle difference</u> between them which <u>you need to know</u>:

> <u>SPEED</u> is just <u>how fast</u> you're going (e.g. 30 mph or 20 m/s) with no regard to the direction.
>
> <u>VELOCITY</u> however must <u>also</u> have the <u>DIRECTION</u> specified, e.g. 30 mph north or 20 m/s, 060°. The distance in a particular direction is called the <u>DISPLACEMENT</u>.

Velocity and displacement are <u>vector quantities</u> — they have magnitude (size) <u>and</u> direction.

Seems kinda fussy I know, but they expect you to remember that distinction, so there you go.

Velocity, Displacement and Time — the Formula:

$$\text{Average velocity} = \frac{\text{Displacement}}{\text{Time}}$$

The '<u>s</u>' here stands for <u>displacement</u>, NOT <u>speed</u>. Don't know why s is used — probably someone's idea of a joke...

You'll often be asked to calculate <u>speed</u> rather than velocity (the words 'speed' and 'velocity' tend to be used interchangeably). It's the <u>same formula</u> — since speed is just velocity without direction...

<u>EXAMPLE:</u>   A cat skulks 20 metres in 35 seconds.
               Find: a) its average speed,   b) how long it takes to skulk 75 m.

<u>ANSWER:</u>   Using the formula triangle:
               a) $v = s/t = 20/35 = 0.5714 = \underline{0.57 \text{ m/s}}$
               b) $t = s/v = 75/0.5714 = 131 \text{ s} = \underline{2 \text{ mins } 11 \text{ s}}$

Speed Cameras Measure the Speed of Cars

1) <u>Speed cameras</u> can be used to catch speeding motorists at <u>dangerous accident spots</u>.
2) <u>Lines</u> are painted on the road a <u>certain distance apart</u> to <u>measure</u> the distance travelled by the car.
3) A <u>photo</u> of the car is taken as it passes the first line and a <u>second photo</u> is taken a <u>certain time later</u>.
4) These photos can then be used to measure the <u>distance travelled</u> by the car in this time.

<u>Example:</u> a speed camera takes two photos of a car. The photos are taken <u>0.5 s</u> apart and from the marked lines on the road the distance it travels is measured as <u>5 m</u>. What is the average speed of the car?

    Answer: Average speed $= \dfrac{\text{distance}}{\text{time}} = \dfrac{5 \text{ m}}{0.5 \text{ s}} = 10 \text{ m/s}$

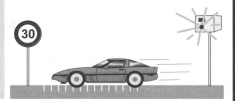

Lights, camera, action — science can be so Hollywood...

Speed cameras aren't the most popular of speed measuring devices. However, most drivers do slow down in speed camera areas and this can improve road safety. Remember, the only <u>difference</u> between speed and velocity is that velocity has <u>direction</u>. They're both calculated in the same way.

Acceleration and Velocity-Time Graphs

Acceleration is How Quickly Velocity is Changing

Acceleration is <u>definitely not</u> the same as <u>velocity</u> or <u>speed</u>.
1) Acceleration is <u>how quickly</u> the velocity is <u>changing</u>.
2) This change in velocity can be a <u>CHANGE IN SPEED</u> or a <u>CHANGE IN DIRECTION</u> or both.
   (You only have to worry about the change in speed bit for calculations.)
Velocity is a simple idea. Acceleration is altogether more <u>subtle</u>, which is why it's <u>confusing</u>.

Acceleration — The Formula:

$$\text{Acceleration} = \frac{\text{Change in Velocity}}{\text{Time taken}}$$

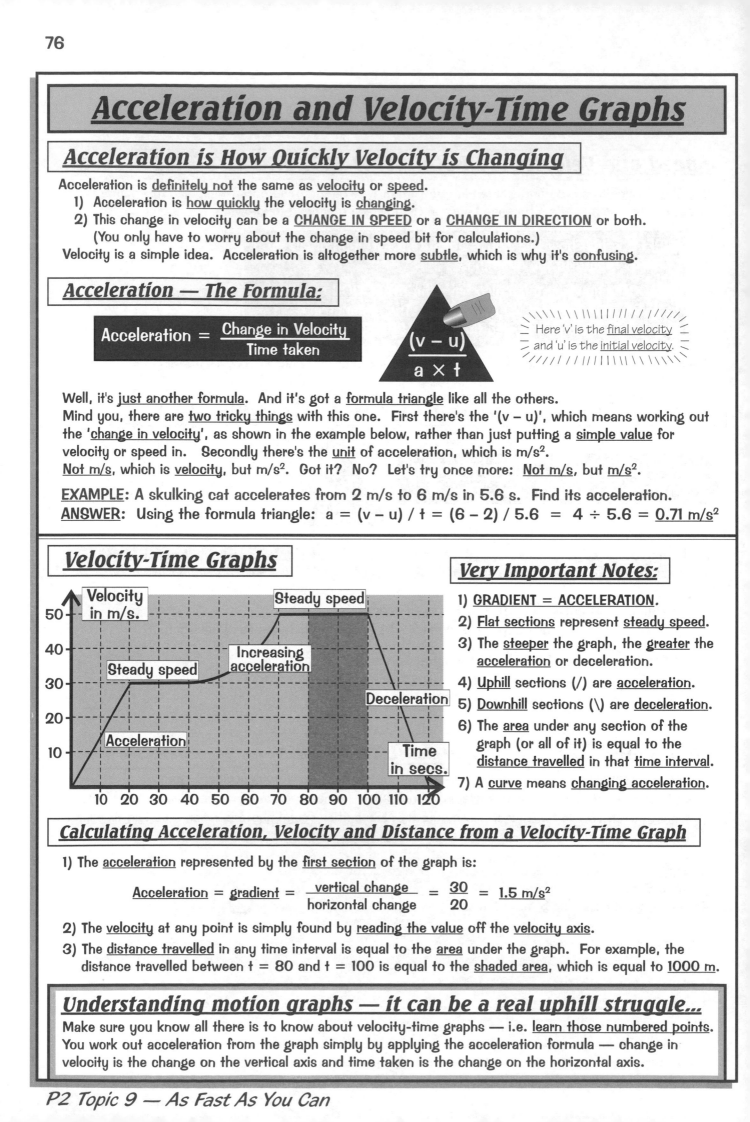

$$\frac{(v - u)}{a \times t}$$

Here 'v' is the <u>final velocity</u> and 'u' is the <u>initial velocity</u>.

Well, it's <u>just another formula</u>. And it's got a <u>formula triangle</u> like all the others.
Mind you, there are <u>two tricky things</u> with this one. First there's the '(v – u)', which means working out the 'change in velocity', as shown in the example below, rather than just putting a <u>simple value</u> for velocity or speed in.   Secondly there's the <u>unit</u> of acceleration, which is m/s².
Not m/s, which is <u>velocity</u>, but m/s²? Got it? No? Let's try once more: <u>Not m/s</u>, but <u>m/s²</u>.

<u>EXAMPLE:</u> A skulking cat accelerates from 2 m/s to 6 m/s in 5.6 s. Find its acceleration.
<u>ANSWER:</u> Using the formula triangle: a = (v – u) / t = (6 – 2) / 5.6 = 4 ÷ 5.6 = <u>0.71 m/s²</u>

Velocity-Time Graphs

Velocity in m/s.

- Steady speed
- Steady speed
- Increasing acceleration
- Acceleration
- Deceleration
- **Time in secs.**

(y-axis: 10, 20, 30, 40, 50; x-axis: 10 20 30 40 50 60 70 80 90 100 110 120)

Very Important Notes:

1) <u>GRADIENT = ACCELERATION</u>.
2) <u>Flat sections</u> represent <u>steady speed</u>.
3) The <u>steeper</u> the graph, the <u>greater</u> the <u>acceleration</u> or deceleration.
4) <u>Uphill</u> sections (/) are <u>acceleration</u>.
5) <u>Downhill</u> sections (\) are <u>deceleration</u>.
6) The <u>area</u> under any section of the graph (or all of it) is equal to the <u>distance travelled</u> in that <u>time interval</u>.
7) A <u>curve</u> means <u>changing acceleration</u>.

Calculating Acceleration, Velocity and Distance from a Velocity-Time Graph

1) The <u>acceleration</u> represented by the <u>first section</u> of the graph is:

$$\text{Acceleration} = \text{gradient} = \frac{\text{vertical change}}{\text{horizontal change}} = \frac{30}{20} = 1.5 \text{ m/s}^2$$

2) The <u>velocity</u> at any point is simply found by <u>reading the value</u> off the <u>velocity axis</u>.

3) The <u>distance travelled</u> in any time interval is equal to the <u>area</u> under the graph. For example, the distance travelled between t = 80 and t = 100 is equal to the <u>shaded area</u>, which is equal to <u>1000 m</u>.

Understanding motion graphs — it can be a real uphill struggle...

Make sure you know all there is to know about velocity-time graphs — i.e. <u>learn those numbered points</u>.
You work out acceleration from the graph simply by applying the acceleration formula — change in velocity is the change on the vertical axis and time taken is the change on the horizontal axis.

Forces

A <u>force</u> is simply a <u>push</u> or a <u>pull</u>. There are only <u>six different forces</u> for you to know about:

1) <u>GRAVITY</u> or <u>WEIGHT</u> always acting <u>straight downwards</u>.
   (On Earth, gravity makes all things <u>accelerate towards the ground</u> at about <u>10 m/s²</u>.)
2) <u>REACTION FORCE</u> from a <u>surface</u>, usually acting <u>straight upwards</u>.
3) <u>THRUST</u> or <u>PUSH</u> or <u>PULL</u> due to an engine or rocket <u>speeding something up</u>.
4) <u>DRAG</u> or <u>AIR RESISTANCE</u> or <u>FRICTION</u> which is <u>slowing the thing down</u>.
5) <u>LIFT</u> due to an <u>aeroplane wing</u>.
6) <u>TENSION</u> in a <u>rope</u> or <u>cable</u>.

And there are basically only <u>five different force diagrams</u>:

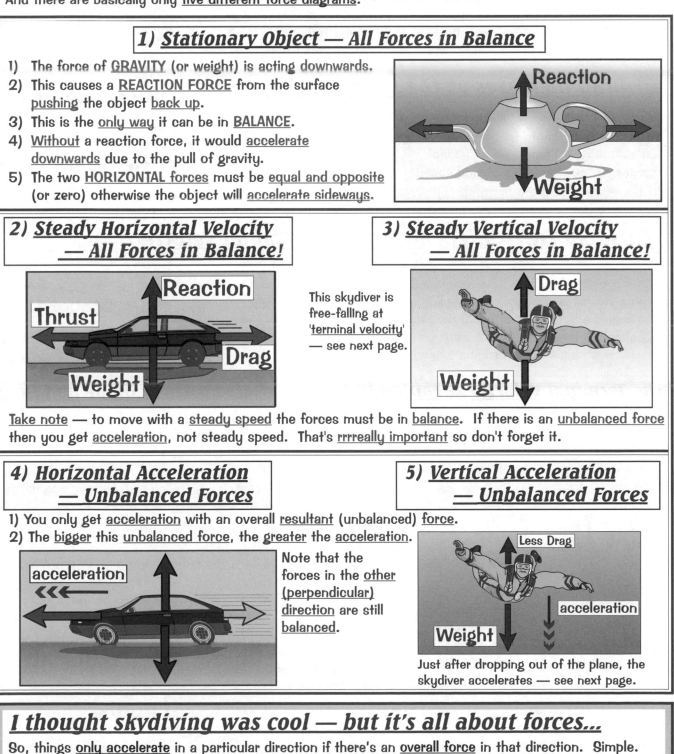

1) *Stationary Object — All Forces in Balance*

1) The force of <u>GRAVITY</u> (or weight) is acting downwards.
2) This causes a <u>REACTION FORCE</u> from the surface <u>pushing</u> the object <u>back up</u>.
3) This is the <u>only way</u> it can be in <u>BALANCE</u>.
4) <u>Without</u> a reaction force, it would <u>accelerate downwards</u> due to the pull of gravity.
5) The two <u>HORIZONTAL</u> forces must be <u>equal and opposite</u> (or zero) otherwise the object will <u>accelerate sideways</u>.

2) *Steady Horizontal Velocity — All Forces in Balance!*

3) *Steady Vertical Velocity — All Forces in Balance!*

This skydiver is free-falling at 'terminal velocity' — see next page.

<u>Take note</u> — to move with a <u>steady speed</u> the forces must be in <u>balance</u>. If there is an <u>unbalanced force</u> then you get <u>acceleration</u>, not steady speed. That's <u>rrrreally important</u> so don't forget it.

4) *Horizontal Acceleration — Unbalanced Forces*

5) *Vertical Acceleration — Unbalanced Forces*

1) You only get <u>acceleration</u> with an overall <u>resultant</u> (unbalanced) <u>force</u>.
2) The <u>bigger</u> this <u>unbalanced force</u>, the <u>greater</u> the <u>acceleration</u>.

Note that the forces in the <u>other</u> (perpendicular) direction are still <u>balanced</u>.

Just after dropping out of the plane, the skydiver accelerates — see next page.

I thought skydiving was cool — but it's all about forces...

So, things <u>only accelerate</u> in a particular direction if there's an <u>overall force</u> in that direction. Simple.

Friction Forces and Terminal Velocity

1) Friction is Always There to Slow Things Down

1) If an object has no force propelling it along it will always slow down and stop because of friction (unless you're in space where there's nothing to rub against).
2) Friction always acts in the opposite direction to movement.
3) To travel at a steady speed, the driving force needs to balance the frictional forces.
4) You get friction between two surfaces in contact, or when an object passes through a fluid (drag).

RESISTANCE OR "DRAG" FROM FLUIDS (AIR OR LIQUID)

The most important factor by far in reducing drag in fluids is keeping the shape of the object streamlined, like fish bodies or boat hulls or bird wings/bodies. The opposite extreme is a parachute which is about as high drag as you can get — which is, of course, the whole idea.

2) Drag Increases as the Speed Increases

Resistance from fluids always increases with speed.
A car has much more friction to work against when travelling at 70 mph compared to 30 mph. So at 70 mph the engine has to work much harder just to maintain a steady speed.
It therefore uses more petrol than it would going just as far at 30 mph.

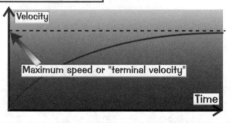

Cars and Free-Fallers All Reach a Terminal Velocity

When cars and free-falling objects first set off they have much more force accelerating them than resistance slowing them down. As the speed increases, the resistance builds up. This gradually reduces the acceleration until eventually the resistance force is equal to the accelerating force and then it won't be able to accelerate any more. It will have reached its maximum speed or terminal velocity.

The Terminal Velocity of Falling Objects Depends on Their Shape and Area

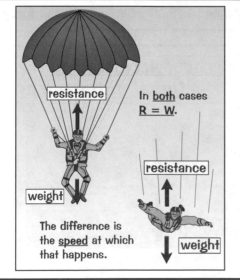

In both cases R = W.

The difference is the speed at which that happens.

The accelerating force acting on all falling objects is gravity and it would make them all fall at the same rate, if it wasn't for air resistance. To prove this, on the Moon, where there's no air, hamsters and feathers dropped simultaneously will hit the ground together. However, on Earth, air resistance causes things to fall at different speeds, and the terminal velocity of any object is determined by its drag in comparison to its weight. The drag depends on its shape and area.

The most important example is the human skydiver. Without his parachute open he has quite a small area and a force of "W = mg" pulling him down. He reaches a terminal velocity of about 120 mph. But with the parachute open, there's much more air resistance (at any given speed) and still only the same force "W = mg" pulling him down. This means his terminal velocity comes right down to about 15 mph, which is a safe speed to hit the ground at.

Learning about air resistance — it can be a real drag...

There are a few really important things on this page. 1) When you fall through a fluid, there's a resistance force (drag), 2) drag increases with speed, so 3) you eventually reach terminal velocity.

Forces and Acceleration

Things only accelerate or change direction if you give them a push. Makes sense.

A Balanced Force Means Steady Speed and Direction

If the forces on an object are all **BALANCED**, then it'll keep moving at the **SAME SPEED** in the **SAME DIRECTION** (so if it starts off still, it'll stay still).

1) When a train or car or bus or anything else is <u>moving</u> at a <u>constant speed</u>, without changing <u>direction</u>, then the <u>forces</u> on it must all be <u>balanced</u>.

2) Never let yourself entertain the <u>ridiculous idea</u> that things need a constant overall force to <u>keep</u> them moving — NO NO NO NO NO NO!

3) To keep going at a <u>steady speed</u>, there must be <u>zero resultant (overall) force</u> — and don't you forget it.

A Resultant Force Means Acceleration

If there is an **UNBALANCED FORCE**, then the object will **ACCELERATE** in the direction of the force. The size of the acceleration is decided by the formula: **F = ma** (see below).

1) An <u>unbalanced force</u> will always produce <u>acceleration</u> (or deceleration).

2) This '<u>acceleration</u>' can take <u>five</u> different forms: <u>starting</u>, <u>stopping</u>, <u>speeding up</u>, <u>slowing down</u> and <u>changing direction</u>.

3) On a <u>force diagram</u>, the <u>arrows</u> will be <u>unequal</u>:

The Overall Unbalanced Force is Often Called the Resultant Force

Any <u>resultant force</u> will produce <u>acceleration</u>, and this is the <u>formula</u> for it:

$$F = ma \quad \text{or} \quad a = F/m$$

m = mass, a = acceleration, F is always the <u>resultant force</u>

Three Points Which Should be Obvious:

1) The bigger the <u>force</u>, the <u>greater</u> the <u>acceleration</u> or <u>deceleration</u>.

2) The bigger the <u>mass</u>, the <u>smaller the acceleration</u>.

3) To get a <u>big mass</u> to accelerate <u>as fast</u> as a <u>small mass</u>, it needs a <u>bigger force</u>. Just think about pushing <u>heavy trolleys</u> and it should all seem <u>fairly obvious</u>, I would hope.

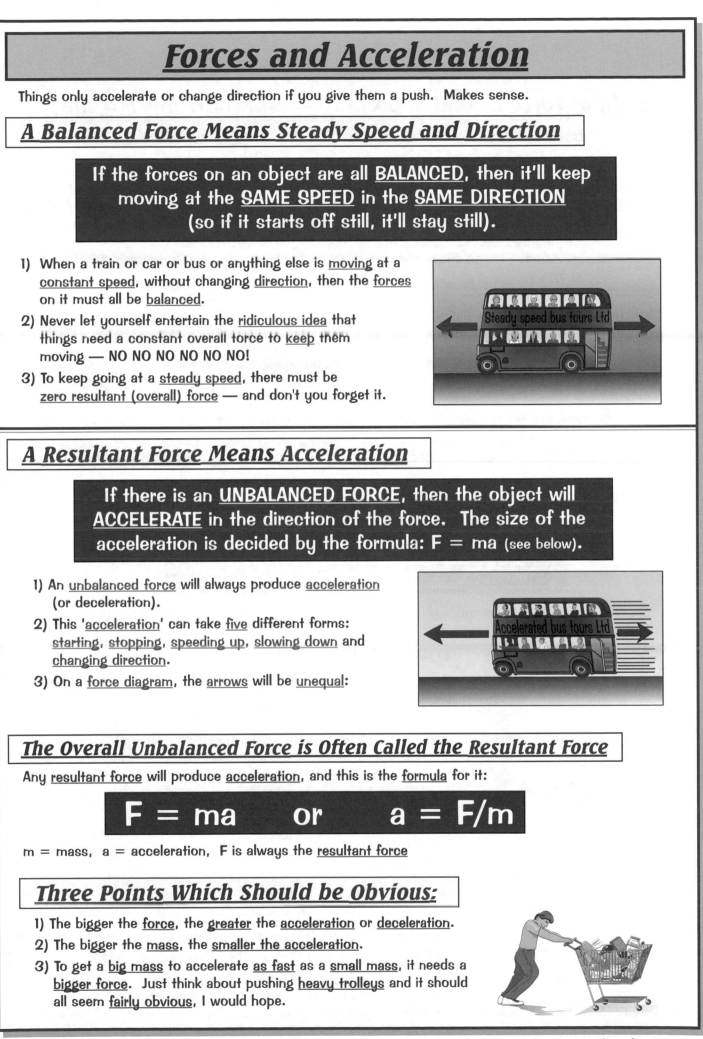

Forces and Acceleration

Resultant Force is Real Important — Especially for "F = ma"

The notion of <u>resultant force</u> is a really important one for you to get your head round.
It's not especially tricky, it's just that it seems to get kind of <u>ignored</u>.
In most <u>real</u> situations there are at least <u>two forces</u> acting on an object along any direction.
The <u>overall</u> effect of these forces will decide the <u>motion</u> of the object — whether it will <u>accelerate</u>,
<u>decelerate</u> or stay at a <u>steady speed</u>. If the forces all point along the same direction, the "<u>overall effect</u>"
is found by just <u>adding or subtracting</u> them. The overall force you get is called the <u>resultant force</u>.
And when you use the <u>formula</u> "<u>F = ma</u>", F must always be the <u>resultant force</u>.

<u>Example:</u>   A car of mass of 1750 kg has an engine which provides a driving force of 5200 N.
            At 70 mph the drag force acting on the car is 5150 N.
            Find its acceleration a) when first setting off from rest b) at 70 mph.

<u>ANSWER:</u> 1) First draw a force diagram for both cases (no need to show the vertical forces):

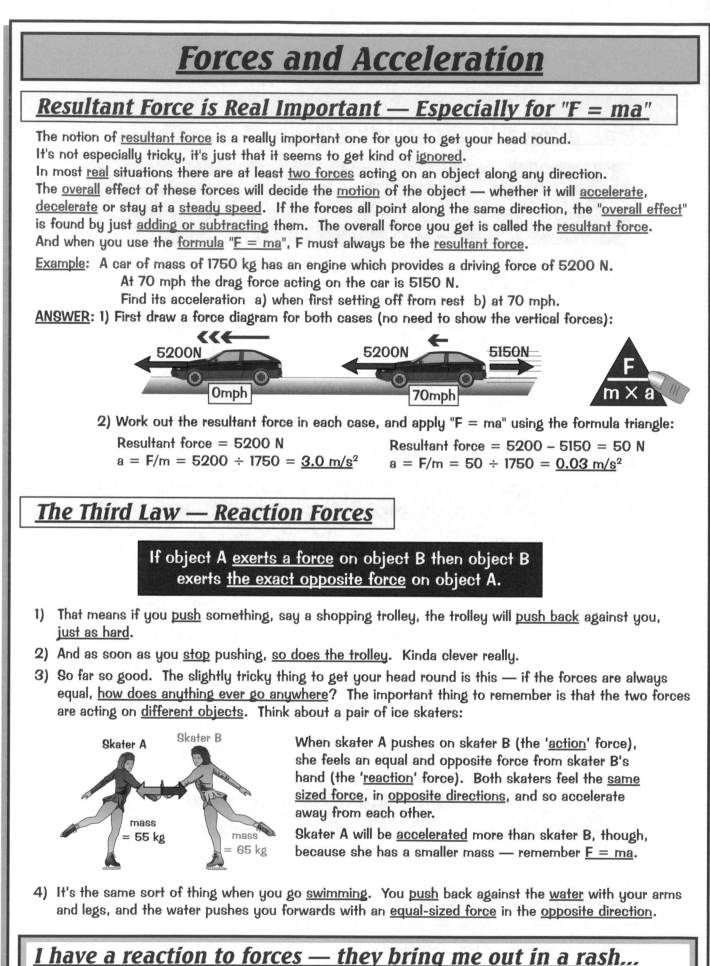

5200N · 0mph   5200N · 70mph · 5150N

2) Work out the resultant force in each case, and apply "F = ma" using the formula triangle:

Resultant force = 5200 N   Resultant force = 5200 − 5150 = 50 N
a = F/m = 5200 ÷ 1750 = <u>**3.0 m/s²**</u>   a = F/m = 50 ÷ 1750 = <u>**0.03 m/s²**</u>

The Third Law — Reaction Forces

> ### If object A <u>exerts a force</u> on object B then object B
> ### exerts <u>the exact opposite force</u> on object A.

1) That means if you <u>push</u> something, say a shopping trolley, the trolley will <u>push back</u> against you,
    <u>just as hard</u>.

2) And as soon as you <u>stop</u> pushing, <u>so does the trolley</u>. Kinda clever really.

3) So far so good. The slightly tricky thing to get your head round is this — if the forces are always
    equal, <u>how does anything ever go anywhere</u>? The important thing to remember is that the two forces
    are acting on <u>different objects</u>. Think about a pair of ice skaters:

Skater A   Skater B

mass = 55 kg   mass = 65 kg

When skater A pushes on skater B (the '<u>action</u>' force),
she feels an equal and opposite force from skater B's
hand (the '<u>reaction</u>' force). Both skaters feel the <u>same</u>
<u>sized force</u>, in <u>opposite directions</u>, and so accelerate
away from each other.

Skater A will be <u>accelerated</u> more than skater B, though,
because she has a smaller mass — remember <u>F = ma</u>.

4) It's the same sort of thing when you go <u>swimming</u>. You <u>push</u> back against the <u>water</u> with your arms
    and legs, and the water pushes you forwards with an <u>equal-sized force</u> in the <u>opposite direction</u>.

I have a reaction to forces — they bring me out in a rash...

This is the real deal. Like... proper Physics. It was <u>pretty fantastic</u> at the time — suddenly people
understood how forces and motion worked, they could work out the <u>orbits of planets</u> and everything.
Inspired? No? Shame. Learn them anyway — you're really going to struggle in the exam if you don't.

Stopping Distances

The stopping distance of a car is the distance covered in the time between the driver <u>first spotting</u> a hazard and the car coming to a <u>complete stop</u>. They're pretty keen on this for exam questions, so make sure you <u>learn it properly</u>.

Many Factors Affect Your Total Stopping Distance

The distance it takes to stop a car is divided into the <u>**THINKING DISTANCE**</u> and the <u>**BRAKING DISTANCE**</u>.

1) Thinking Distance

"The distance the car travels in the time between the driver noticing the hazard and applying the brakes."

It's affected by <u>**TWO MAIN FACTORS**</u>:

a) <u>How FAST you're going</u> — obviously. Whatever your reaction time, the <u>faster</u> you're going, the <u>further</u> you'll go.

b) <u>How DOPEY you are</u> — This is affected by <u>tiredness</u>, <u>drugs</u>, <u>alcohol</u>, <u>old age</u>, and a <u>careless</u> blasé attitude.

The figures below for typical stopping distances are from the Highway Code. It's frightening to see just how far it takes to stop when you're going at 70 mph.

2) Braking Distance

"The distance the car travels during its deceleration whilst the brakes are being applied".

It's affected by <u>**FOUR MAIN FACTORS**</u>:

a) <u>How FAST you're going</u> — the <u>faster</u> you're going, the <u>further</u> it takes to stop.

b) <u>How HEAVILY LOADED the vehicle is</u> — with the <u>same</u> brakes, a <u>heavily laden</u> vehicle takes <u>longer to stop</u>. A car won't stop as quick when it's full of people and luggage and towing a caravan.

c) <u>How good your BRAKES are</u> — all brakes must be checked and maintained <u>regularly</u>. Worn or faulty brakes will let you down <u>catastrophically</u> just when you need them the <u>most</u>, i.e. in an <u>emergency</u>.

d) <u>How good the GRIP is</u> — this depends on <u>**THREE THINGS**</u>:

1) <u>road surface</u>, 2) <u>weather</u> conditions, 3) <u>tyres</u>.

So even at <u>30 mph</u>, you should drive no closer than <u>6 or 7 car lengths</u> away from the car in front — just in case. This is why <u>speed limits</u> are so important, and some <u>residential areas</u> are now <u>20 mph zones</u>.

Leaves and diesel spills and muck on t'road are <u>serious hazards</u> because they're <u>unexpected</u>. <u>Wet</u> or <u>icy roads</u> are always much more <u>slippy</u> than dry roads, but often you only discover this when you try to <u>brake</u> hard! Tyres should have a minimum <u>tread depth</u> of <u>1.6 mm</u>. This is essential for getting rid of the <u>water</u> in wet conditions. Without <u>tread</u>, a tyre will simply <u>ride</u> on a <u>layer of water</u> and skid <u>very easily</u>. This is called "<u>aquaplaning</u>" and isn't nearly as cool as it sounds.

<u>Bad visibility</u> can also be a major factor in accidents — lashing rain, thick fog, bright oncoming lights, etc. might mean that a driver <u>doesn't notice</u> a hazard until they're quite close to it — so they have a much shorter distance available to stop in.

Chart labels:
30 mph — 9 m, 14 m, 6 car lengths
50 mph — 15 m, 38 m, 13 car lengths
70 mph — 21 m, 75 m, 24 car lengths
Thinking distance
Braking distance

Stop right there — and learn this page...

Scary stuff. Makes you think doesn't it. Learn all the details and write yourself a <u>mini-essay</u> to see how much you really know. You might have to interpret charts of stopping distance in your exam.

Car Safety

A <u>large</u> rugby player running very <u>fast</u> is going to be a lot harder to stop than a scrawny one out for a Sunday afternoon stroll — that's momentum for you.

Momentum = Mass × Velocity

1) The <u>greater</u> the <u>mass</u> of an object and the <u>greater</u> its <u>velocity</u>, the <u>more momentum</u> the object has.

2) Momentum is a <u>vector</u> quantity — it has size <u>and</u> direction (like <u>velocity</u>, but not speed).

Momentum (kg m/s) = Mass (kg) × Velocity (m/s)

Forces Cause Changes in Momentum

1) When a <u>force</u> acts on an object, it causes a <u>change</u> in momentum.

$$\text{Force acting (N)} = \frac{\text{Change in Momentum (kg m/s)}}{\text{Time taken for change to happen (s)}}$$

2) A <u>larger</u> force means a <u>faster</u> change of momentum (and so a greater <u>acceleration</u>).

3) Likewise, if someone's momentum changes <u>very quickly</u> (like in a <u>car crash</u>), the <u>forces</u> on the body will be very <u>large</u> (and more likely to cause <u>injury</u>).

4) This is why cars are designed to slow people down over a <u>longer time</u> when they have a crash — the longer it takes for a change in <u>momentum</u>, the <u>smaller</u> the <u>force</u>.

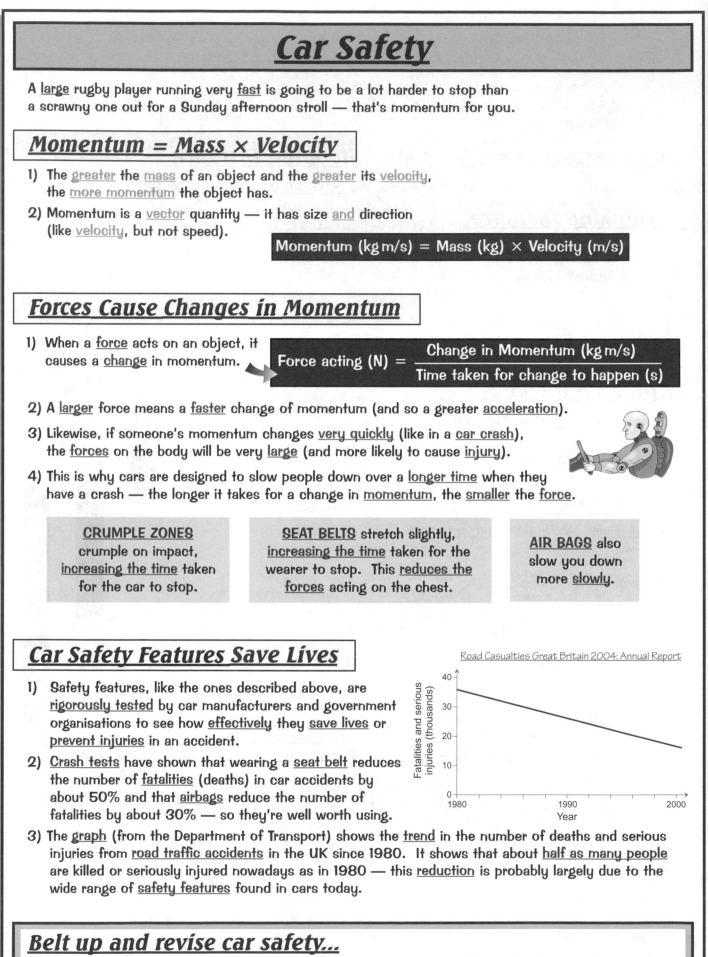

| **CRUMPLE ZONES** crumple on impact, <u>increasing the time</u> taken for the car to stop. | **SEAT BELTS** stretch slightly, <u>increasing the time</u> taken for the wearer to stop. This <u>reduces the forces</u> acting on the chest. | **AIR BAGS** also slow you down more <u>slowly</u>. |

Car Safety Features Save Lives

1) Safety features, like the ones described above, are <u>rigorously tested</u> by car manufacturers and government organisations to see how <u>effectively</u> they <u>save lives</u> or <u>prevent injuries</u> in an accident.

2) <u>Crash tests</u> have shown that wearing a <u>seat belt</u> reduces the number of <u>fatalities</u> (deaths) in car accidents by about **50%** and that <u>airbags</u> reduce the number of fatalities by about **30%** — so they're well worth using.

Road Casualties Great Britain 2004: Annual Report

3) The <u>graph</u> (from the Department of Transport) shows the <u>trend</u> in the number of deaths and serious injuries from <u>road traffic accidents</u> in the UK since 1980. It shows that about <u>half as many people</u> are killed or seriously injured nowadays as in 1980 — this <u>reduction</u> is probably largely due to the wide range of <u>safety features</u> found in cars today.

Belt up and revise car safety...

Passengers in the back of cars who don't wear a seat belt will hit the front seat with a force of between <u>30 to 60 times</u> their body's weight in an accident at 30 mph — this is like the force you'd feel if you were sat on by an <u>elephant</u> (which I really wouldn't recommend).

Taking Risks

A 'risk' is just the probability of something bad happening.

You Can Work Out the Risk of Something Happening

1) You can <u>estimate</u> the <u>risk</u> of something happening based on <u>how many times</u> it's happened in the <u>past</u> — 'statistical risk assessment'. The <u>more data</u> you have to base the estimate on, the more <u>accurate</u> your risk assessment is likely to be.

2) Or you can use a <u>scientific theory</u> to <u>model</u> the situation, then <u>calculate</u> the probability. Simple example — if you're playing a game with dice or cards, you can calculate the risk of losing.

3) Generally, risk assessors use a <u>combination</u> of the two to get the <u>best possible estimate</u>.

4) The <u>size</u> of a risk can be expressed as a <u>fraction</u>, a <u>decimal</u> or a <u>percentage</u>. You need to be able to <u>convert</u> between them for the exam:

> <u>Example:</u> The risk of Simon falling into a ditch on the way home from Buffers nightclub is 1 in 500. Write this risk as a fraction, a decimal and a percentage.
>
> > '1 in 500' means the fraction 1/500.
> >
> > To convert a <u>FRACTION</u> to a <u>DECIMAL</u>, just <u>divide</u> (use your calculator): $1 \div 500 = 0.002$
> >
> > To convert a <u>DECIMAL</u> to a <u>PERCENTAGE</u>, <u>multiply by 100</u>: $0.002 \times 100 = 0.2\%$.

If you need to <u>compare</u> the sizes of different risks, the easiest way is to <u>convert</u> them all into <u>decimals first</u>. Then, obviously, the <u>smaller</u> the number, the <u>smaller</u> the risk:

> <u>Example:</u> Claire compared the effectiveness of the safety features of three different models of car using data from crash tests. The tests assessed the risk of suffering fatal injuries in a head-on collision at 35 mph with another car. The risks were stated as follows:
>
> > Model X — 0.1   Model Y — 3/20   Model Z — 20%
>
> Which model is safest in this type of collision?
>
> > Model X is already in decimal form, but you need to convert the other two.
> >
> > Model Y: $3 \div 20 = 0.15$ (divide to turn a fraction into a decimal)
> >
> > Model Z: $20 \div 100 = 0.2$ (divide by 100 to turn a percentage into a decimal)
> >
> > So, <u>Model X</u> would be safest.

People are a Bit Weird When It Comes to Taking Risks

The reasons why people take risks are quite <u>complex</u> and often don't make a lot of sense. Your <u>willingness</u> to take a risk can be influenced by many factors including:

1) The degree of <u>familiarity</u> — many people don't feel at risk travelling by car because it's something they do all the time. Whereas travelling by plane can seem much more 'risky'.

2) Whether you are <u>forced</u> to take a risk or <u>choose</u> to.

3) Whether you feel <u>in control</u> of the situation — many people feel that driving a car is safer than flying because they are in control.

4) The <u>possible rewards</u> — some people are quite happy to take part in a dangerous sport such as skiing because they know they'll enjoy it so much. Similarly, you might take a risk on a financial investment because there's a chance you'll make lots of money.

5) <u>Personal experiences</u> — If someone you know had a nasty bungee jumping accident, you're probably not going to be too keen to try it yourself.

6) <u>Age or personality type</u> — some people just like to take risks and some don't.

Revise well — it'll reduce the risk of exam failure...

So risks can be calculated and compared, and taken or not taken. Make sure you follow the examples.

Revision Summary for P2 Topic 9

More jolly questions which I know you're going to really enjoy. There are lots of bits and bobs about forces and motion which you definitely have to learn. You know what to do with the tricky questions — read over the relevant stuff again, then have another go at them. Keep at it till you can do every question.

1) Write down the formula for working out velocity.

2)* Find the speed of a partly chewed mouse which hobbles 3.2 metres in 35 seconds.
Find how far he would go in 25 minutes.

3)* A speed camera is set up in a 30 mph (13.4 m/s) zone. It takes two photographs 0.5 s apart.
A car travels 6.3 m between the two photographs. Was the car breaking the speed limit?

4) What is acceleration? What is the unit used?

5)* Write down the formula for acceleration. What's the acceleration of a soggy pea flicked from rest to a speed of 14 m/s in 0.4 seconds?

6) Sketch a typical velocity-time graph and point out all the important parts.

7) Explain how to find velocity, distance and acceleration from a velocity-time graph.

8) Name six different types of force.

9) Sketch five standard force diagrams, showing the forces and the types of motion.

10) Describe how friction is affected by speed.

11) Describe the effect on the top speed of a car of adding a roof box. Explain your answer.

12) What is "terminal velocity"? What two main factors affect the terminal velocity of a falling object?

13) If an object has zero resultant force on it, can it be moving? Can it be accelerating?

14)* Write down the formula relating resultant force and acceleration. A force of 30 N pushes a trolley of mass 4 kg. What will be its acceleration?

15) Explain what a reaction force is and where it pops up.

16) What are the two different parts of the overall stopping distance of a car?

17) List two factors which affect each of the two parts of the stopping distance.

18) If you're driving at 50 mph, how many car lengths away from the car in front should you be?

19) Describe what "aquaplaning" means.

20)* Write down the formula for momentum. Find the momentum of a 78 kg sheep falling at 15 m/s.

21) What effect does an increase in the resultant force have on the momentum of an object?

22)* A gymnast (mass 50 kg) jumps off a beam and hits the floor at a speed of 7 m/s.
She bends her knees and stops moving in 0.5 s. What is the average force acting on her?

23) Explain how seatbelts, crumple zones and airbags are useful in a crash.

24) Give two methods of estimating the risk of something happening.

25)* Geoff wants to buy a new shed. He researches five different types of shed and finds out the following information:

SHED	RISK OF COLLAPSE IN FIRST THREE YEARS
1	$\frac{3}{5}$
2	0.03
3	5%
4	0.012
5	$\frac{12}{96}$

Geoff wants to buy the sturdiest shed.
Which one should he choose?

* Answers on page 106

Work and Kinetic Energy

When a force moves an object, energy is transferred and work is done.

That statement sounds far more complicated than it needs to. Try this:

1) Whenever something <u>moves</u>, something else is providing some sort of 'effort' to move it.

2) The thing putting the <u>effort</u> in needs a <u>supply</u> of energy (like <u>fuel</u> or <u>food</u> or <u>electricity</u> etc.).

3) It then does '<u>work</u>' by <u>moving</u> the object — and one way or another it <u>transfers</u> the energy it receives (as fuel etc.) into <u>other forms</u>.

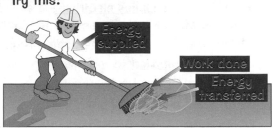

4) Whether this energy is transferred '<u>usefully</u>' (e.g. by <u>lifting a load</u>) or is '<u>wasted</u>' (e.g. lost as <u>friction</u>), you can still say that '<u>work is done</u>'. Just like Batman and Bruce Wayne, '<u>work done</u>' and '<u>energy transferred</u>' are indeed '<u>one and the same</u>'. (And they're both given in <u>joules</u>.)

It's Just Another Trivial Formula:

Work Done = Force × Distance

Whether the force is <u>friction</u> or <u>weight</u> or <u>tension in a rope</u>, it's always the same. To find how much <u>energy</u> has been <u>transferred</u> (in joules), you just multiply the <u>force in N</u> by the <u>distance moved in m</u>. Easy as that. I'll show you...

<u>Example:</u> Some hooligan kids drag an old tractor tyre 5 m over rough ground. They pull with a total force of 340 N. Find the energy transferred.
<u>Answer:</u> W = F × s = 340 × 5 = <u>1700 J</u>. Phew — easy peasy isn't it?

Kinetic Energy is Energy of Movement

Anything which is <u>moving</u> has <u>kinetic energy</u>.
There's a slightly <u>tricky formula</u> for it, so you have to concentrate a little bit <u>harder</u> for this one. But hey, that's life — it can be real tough sometimes:

Kinetic Energy = ½ × mass × velocity^2

<u>EXAMPLE:</u> A car of mass 2450 kg is travelling at 38 m/s.
Calculate its kinetic energy.
<u>ANSWER:</u> It's pretty easy. You just plug the numbers into the formula — but watch the "v^2"!
KE = ½mv^2 = ½ × 2450 × 38^2 = <u>1 768 900 J</u> (joules because it's <u>energy</u>)
(When the car stops suddenly, nearly all this energy is dissipated as heat in the brakes — it's a lot of heat.)

Remember, the <u>kinetic energy</u> of something depends both on <u>mass</u> and <u>speed</u>.
The <u>more it weighs</u> and the <u>faster it's going</u>, the <u>bigger</u> its kinetic energy will be.

small mass, not fast
low kinetic energy

big fast
lorries Ltd

big mass, real fast
high kinetic energy

Revise energy — keep working at it...

Moving things have <u>kinetic energy</u>, which is proportional to <u>speed squared</u>. This means that if object A is travelling at twice the speed of an identical object B, it will have four times as much kinetic energy (not twice as much). So it takes four times the distance to dissipate the energy (i.e. to stop). That's why the braking distance (see p81) for a car going at 60 mph is four times further than for a car going at 30 mph.

Electrical and Potential Energy

Electrical Power Sources Supply Electrical Energy

Anything which <u>supplies electricity</u> is also supplying <u>electrical energy</u>. So cells, batteries, generators etc. all <u>transfer energy</u> to components in the circuit.

1) When an electrical <u>charge</u> goes through a <u>change</u> in voltage, <u>energy</u> is <u>transferred</u>.
2) Energy is <u>supplied</u> to the charge at the <u>power source</u> to raise it through a voltage.
3) The charge <u>gives up</u> this energy when it <u>passes</u> through <u>components</u> in the circuit.

The formula for electrical energy is:

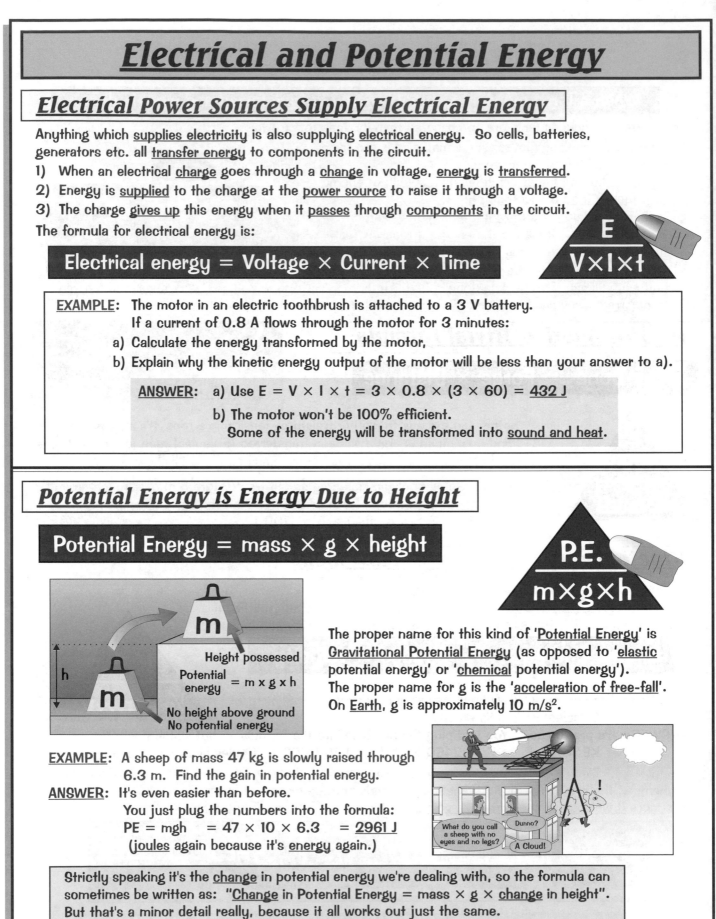

$$\text{Electrical energy} = \text{Voltage} \times \text{Current} \times \text{Time}$$

$$\frac{E}{V \times I \times t}$$

> **EXAMPLE:** The motor in an electric toothbrush is attached to a 3 V battery.
> If a current of 0.8 A flows through the motor for 3 minutes:
> a) Calculate the energy transformed by the motor,
> b) Explain why the kinetic energy output of the motor will be less than your answer to a).
>
> > **ANSWER:** a) Use $E = V \times I \times t = 3 \times 0.8 \times (3 \times 60) = \underline{432\ J}$
> >
> > b) The motor won't be 100% efficient.
> > Some of the energy will be transformed into <u>sound and heat</u>.

Potential Energy is Energy Due to Height

$$\text{Potential Energy} = \text{mass} \times g \times \text{height}$$

$$\frac{P.E.}{m \times g \times h}$$

Height possessed
Potential energy $= m \times g \times h$

No height above ground
No potential energy

The proper name for this kind of '<u>Potential Energy</u>' is <u>Gravitational Potential Energy</u> (as opposed to '<u>elastic</u> potential energy' or '<u>chemical</u> potential energy').
The proper name for g is the '<u>acceleration of free-fall</u>'.
On <u>Earth</u>, g is approximately <u>10 m/s²</u>.

What do you call a sheep with no eyes and no legs? | Dunno? | A Cloud!

EXAMPLE: A sheep of mass 47 kg is slowly raised through 6.3 m. Find the gain in potential energy.
ANSWER: It's even easier than before.
You just plug the numbers into the formula:
PE = mgh $= 47 \times 10 \times 6.3 = \underline{2961\ J}$
(<u>joules</u> again because it's <u>energy</u> again.)

> Strictly speaking it's the <u>change</u> in potential energy we're dealing with, so the formula can sometimes be written as: "<u>Change</u> in Potential Energy = mass $\times$ g $\times$ <u>change</u> in height". But that's a minor detail really, because it all works out just the same.

I'd say this page is electric — hmmm, it's got the potential...

Remember, energy transfer is rarely <u>100% efficient</u> (although the total amount of energy is conserved). For example, you'll notice that your **TV** heats up if it's been on a while (some electrical energy is lost as heat energy), and when you boil the kettle energy is lost as sound and as heat to the room.

Conservation of Energy

There are Two Types of "Energy Conservation"

Try and get your head round the difference between these two.

1) "ENERGY CONSERVATION" is all about <u>using less fossil fuels</u> because of the damage it does and because they might <u>run out</u>. That's all <u>environmental stuff</u> — important to us but fairly trivial on a <u>cosmic scale</u>.

2) The "<u>PRINCIPLE OF THE CONSERVATION OF ENERGY</u>", on the other hand, is one of the <u>major cornerstones</u> of physics. It's an <u>all-pervading principle</u> which governs the workings of the <u>entire physical Universe</u>. If this principle were not so, then life as we know it would simply cease to be.

3) Got it now? Good. <u>Well don't forget</u>.

The Principle of the Conservation of Energy Can be Stated Thus:

> Energy can never be created nor destroyed — only converted from one form to another.

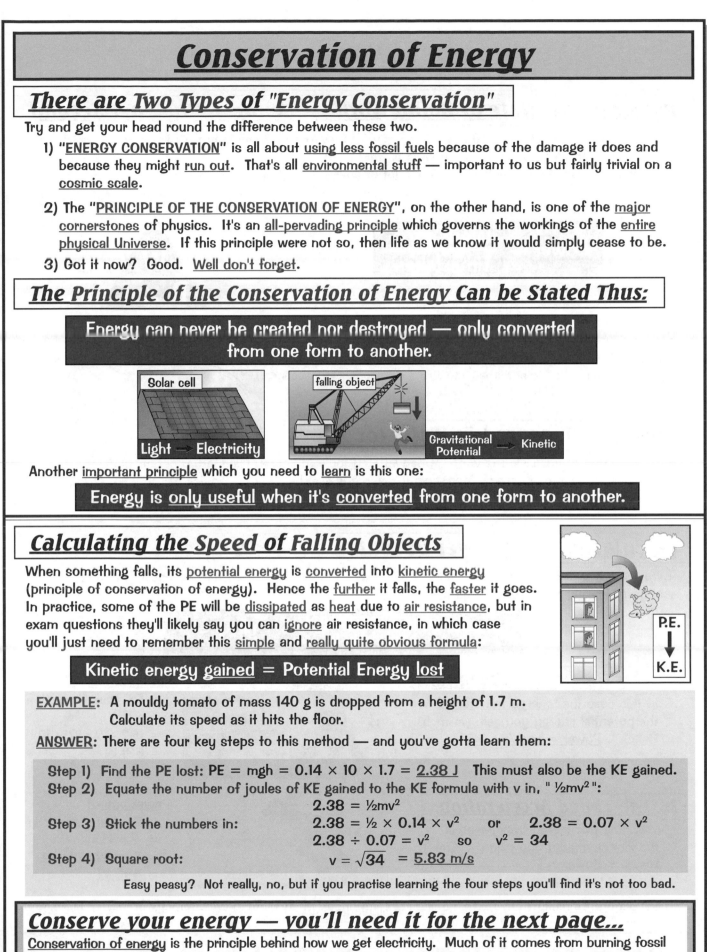

Light → Electricity

falling object

Gravitational Potential → Kinetic

Another <u>important principle</u> which you need to <u>learn</u> is this one:

> Energy is <u>only useful</u> when it's <u>converted</u> from one form to another.

Calculating the Speed of Falling Objects

When something falls, its <u>potential energy</u> is <u>converted</u> into <u>kinetic energy</u> (principle of conservation of energy). Hence the <u>further</u> it falls, the <u>faster</u> it goes. In practice, some of the PE will be <u>dissipated</u> as <u>heat</u> due to <u>air resistance</u>, but in exam questions they'll likely say you can <u>ignore</u> air resistance, in which case you'll just need to remember this <u>simple</u> and <u>really quite obvious</u> formula:

P.E. ↓ K.E.

> Kinetic energy <u>gained</u> = Potential Energy <u>lost</u>

<u>EXAMPLE:</u> A mouldy tomato of mass 140 g is dropped from a height of 1.7 m. Calculate its speed as it hits the floor.

<u>ANSWER:</u> There are four key steps to this method — and you've gotta learn them:

Step 1) Find the PE lost: PE = mgh = 0.14 × 10 × 1.7 = <u>2.38 J</u>   This must also be the KE gained.

Step 2) Equate the number of joules of KE gained to the KE formula with v in, " $\frac{1}{2}mv^2$ ":
$$2.38 = \tfrac{1}{2}mv^2$$

Step 3) Stick the numbers in: $2.38 = \tfrac{1}{2} \times 0.14 \times v^2$ or $2.38 = 0.07 \times v^2$
$$2.38 \div 0.07 = v^2 \quad \text{so} \quad v^2 = 34$$

Step 4) Square root: $v = \sqrt{34}$ = <u>5.83 m/s</u>

Easy peasy? Not really, no, but if you practise learning the four steps you'll find it's not too bad.

Conserve your energy — you'll need it for the next page...

<u>Conservation of energy</u> is the principle behind how we get electricity. Much of it comes from burning fossil fuels — power stations convert chemical energy in the fuel to electrical energy. These days, alas, <u>energy conservation</u> is also a big issue. Burning fossil fuels contributes to global warming and, anyway, one day they'll run out. So we need to be more efficient with our energy, and look at other forms of energy transfer to produce electricity — e.g. wind turbines which convert kinetic energy from the wind to electrical energy.

Power

Power is the "Rate of Doing Work" — i.e. How Much per Second

Power is not the same thing as force, nor energy. A powerful machine is not necessarily one which can exert a strong force (though it usually ends up that way).

A powerful machine is one which transfers a lot of energy in a short space of time.

This is the very easy formula for power:

$$\text{Power} = \frac{\text{Work done}}{\text{Time taken}}$$

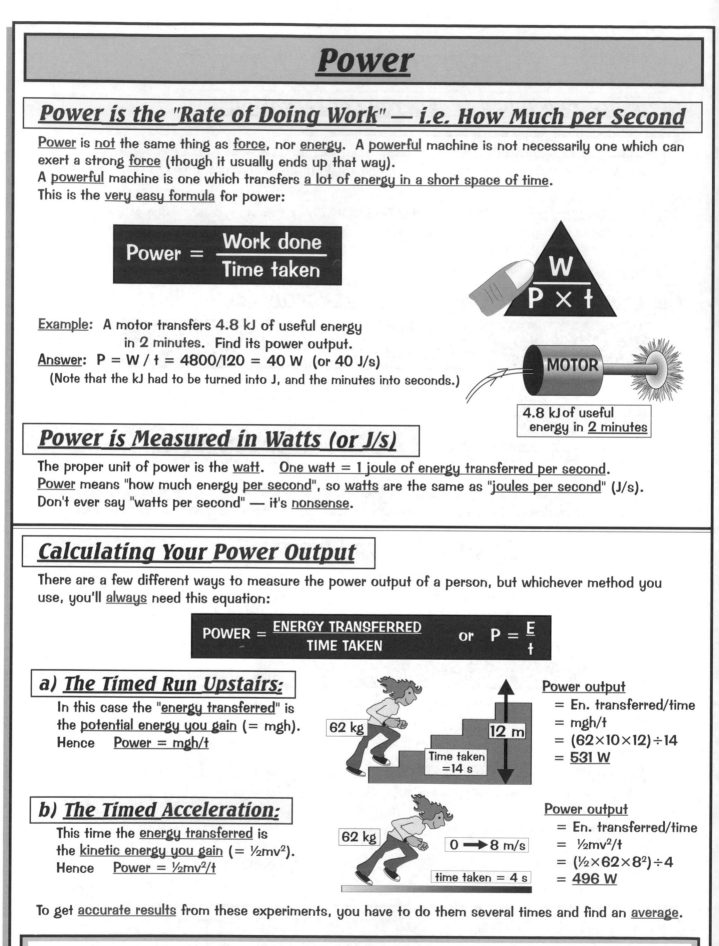

Example: A motor transfers 4.8 kJ of useful energy in 2 minutes. Find its power output.

Answer: $P = W / t = 4800/120 = 40 \text{ W}$ (or 40 J/s)

(Note that the kJ had to be turned into J, and the minutes into seconds.)

4.8 kJ of useful energy in 2 minutes

Power is Measured in Watts (or J/s)

The proper unit of power is the watt. One watt = 1 joule of energy transferred per second.

Power means "how much energy per second", so watts are the same as "joules per second" (J/s).

Don't ever say "watts per second" — it's nonsense.

Calculating Your Power Output

There are a few different ways to measure the power output of a person, but whichever method you use, you'll always need this equation:

$$\text{POWER} = \frac{\text{ENERGY TRANSFERRED}}{\text{TIME TAKEN}} \quad \text{or} \quad P = \frac{E}{t}$$

a) _The Timed Run Upstairs:_

In this case the "energy transferred" is the potential energy you gain (= mgh).

Hence   Power = mgh/t

62 kg

12 m

Time taken =14 s

Power output
= En. transferred/time
= mgh/t
= $(62 \times 10 \times 12) \div 14$
= __531 W__

b) _The Timed Acceleration:_

This time the energy transferred is the kinetic energy you gain (= ½mv²).

Hence   Power = ½mv²/t

62 kg

0 ➡ 8 m/s

time taken = 4 s

Power output
= En. transferred/time
= ½mv²/t
= $(½ \times 62 \times 8^2) \div 4$
= __496 W__

To get accurate results from these experiments, you have to do them several times and find an average.

Power — you need to know watts watt...

Power is the amount of energy transferred per second, and it's measured in watts. The watt is named after James Watt, a Scottish inventor and engineer who did a lot of work on steam engines in the 1700s. Nice. Make sure you learn the formula and power questions should be a doddle.

Circular Motion

If it wasn't for <u>circular</u> motion our little planet would just be wandering aimlessly around the Universe. And as soon as you launched a <u>satellite</u>, it'd just go flying off into space. Hardly ideal.

Circular Motion — Velocity is Constantly Changing

1) Velocity is both the speed and direction of an object.

2) If an object is travelling in a circle it is <u>constantly changing direction</u>, which means it's <u>accelerating</u>.

3) This means there <u>must</u> be a <u>force</u> acting on it (F = ma).

4) This force acts towards the centre of the circle and is called a <u>centripetal force</u>.

pronounced sen-tree-pee-tal

The velocity's in this direction, but...

...the force is always towards the centre of the circle.

In the exam, you can be asked to say <u>which force</u> is actually providing the centripetal force in a given situation. It can be <u>tension</u>, or <u>friction</u>, or even <u>gravity</u>.

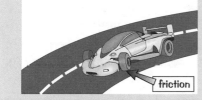

<u>A car going round a bend:</u>

1) Imagine the bend is part of a <u>circle</u> — the centripetal force is towards the <u>centre</u> of the circle.

2) The force is from <u>friction</u> between the car's tyres and the road.

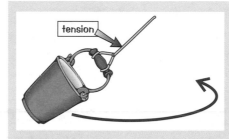

<u>A bucket whirling round on a rope:</u>
The centripetal force comes from <u>tension in the rope</u>. Break the rope, and the bucket flies off at a tangent.

<u>A satellite orbiting Earth:</u>
The centripetal force keeping the satellite in a circular orbit is the <u>gravitational force</u> between Earth and the satellite.

Centripetal Force Depends on Mass, Speed and Radius

1) The <u>faster</u> an object's moving, the <u>bigger</u> the centripetal force has to be to keep it moving in a <u>circle</u>.

2) Likewise, the <u>heavier</u> the object, the <u>bigger</u> the centripetal force has to be to keep it moving in a <u>circle</u>.

3) And you need a <u>larger force</u> to keep something moving in a <u>smaller circle</u> (i.e. with a smaller radius) — as it has 'more turning' to do.

It's physics, so there must be an <u>equation</u>... and here it is — it's a beauty...

$$\text{Centripetal Force (N)} = \frac{\text{Mass (kg)} \times \text{Speed}^2}{\text{Radius (m)}} \qquad F = \frac{mv^2}{r}$$

EXAMPLE: A racing car of mass 600 kg is driving around a circular track of radius 200 m, at a speed of 40 m/s. Calculate the centripetal force.

ANSWER: Just stick the numbers into the equation: $F = \frac{mv^2}{r} = \frac{600 \times 40^2}{200} = \frac{960\,000}{200} = \underline{4800\ N}$. Easy.

This idea of centripetal force explains why you need to drive more slowly round bends when it's raining than when it's dry. The more water there is on the road, the less friction there is between the car's tyres and the road. Less friction means less centripetal force. So unless your speed is reduced, the centripetal force won't be enough to stop you spinning off.

Circular motion — get round to learning it...

To understand this, you need to learn that <u>constant change in direction means constant acceleration</u>. Velocity is a vector — it has direction, and acceleration is change in velocity. When there's acceleration, there's force (see, easy). Learn what forces can provide centripetal force — tension, friction etc.

Roller Coasters

Roller Coasters Transfer Energy

This is similar to the falling object example on page 87.

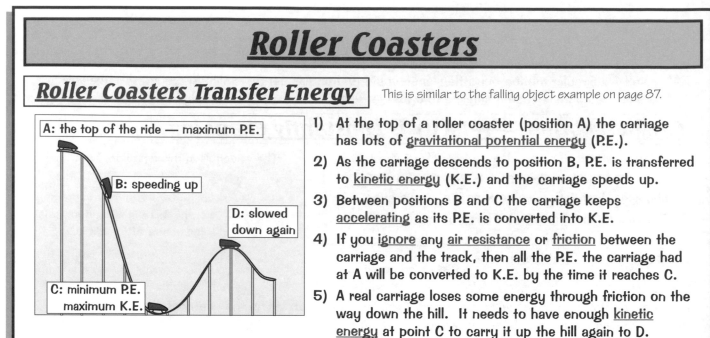

A: the top of the ride — maximum P.E.

B: speeding up

D: slowed down again

C: minimum P.E. maximum K.E.

1) At the top of a roller coaster (position A) the carriage has lots of <u>gravitational potential energy</u> (P.E.).

2) As the carriage descends to position B, P.E. is transferred to <u>kinetic energy</u> (K.E.) and the carriage speeds up.

3) Between positions B and C the carriage keeps <u>accelerating</u> as its P.E. is converted into K.E.

4) If you <u>ignore</u> any <u>air resistance</u> or <u>friction</u> between the carriage and the track, then all the P.E. the carriage had at A will be converted to K.E. by the time it reaches C.

5) A real carriage loses some energy through friction on the way down the hill. It needs to have enough <u>kinetic energy</u> at point C to carry it up the hill again to D.

<u>EXAM-STYLE QUESTION</u>: Look at the diagram above. Let's say that the vertical drop between positions A and D is 20 m. What is the maximum speed of the carriage at position D? Take gravity to be 10 N/kg.

<u>ANSWER</u>: Assuming no friction, the K.E. gained between A and D is equal to the P.E. lost. Turning this into an equation gives $\frac{1}{2}mv^2 = mgh$, which rearranges to $v^2 = 2gh = 2 \times 10 \times 20$, so $v^2 = 400$ and $v = 20$ m/s.

To Loop the Loop You Need a Centripetal Force

1) When you <u>loop the loop</u> you feel heavier at the bottom of the loop than you do at the top. What you're feeling is a <u>reaction force</u> (see p.80).

2) During the loop two <u>forces</u> are acting on you:
   i) Your <u>weight</u> always acts towards the ground (sometimes that's towards the centre of the loop, sometimes it's away from the centre).
   ii) A <u>reaction force</u> from your seat which always acts towards the centre of the loop, at right angles to the track.

3) These two forces combine to give a <u>resultant centripetal force</u> (see previous page). The two simplest cases are when you're at the very top and the very bottom of the loop.

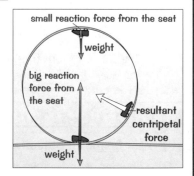

small reaction force from the seat

weight

big reaction force from the seat

weight

resultant centripetal force

4) At the <u>top</u> of the loop, both <u>weight</u> and <u>reaction force</u> are acting in the <u>same direction</u>, so:

centripetal force = reaction + weight ⇒ REACTION = CENTRIPETAL FORCE − WEIGHT

That means you only feel a gentle force from your seat, that is, you feel 'light'. In fact, if the centripetal force and your weight are equal, there's <u>no reaction force at all</u> and you feel '<u>weightless</u>'.

5) At the <u>bottom</u> of the loop, the two forces are acting in <u>opposite directions</u>, so:

centripetal force = reaction − weight ⇒ REACTION = CENTRIPETAL FORCE + WEIGHT

So you feel much '<u>heavier</u>' at the bottom of the loop than you do at the top.

Designers have to think about SAFETY and the LOCAL COMMUNITY when designing rides

❶ <u>SAFETY FEATURES</u>: These can be built into the rides themselves, e.g. <u>headrests</u> and <u>seatbelts</u>. Or there might be safety restrictions on the people who can go on a ride, e.g. <u>height restrictions</u>.

❷ <u>SOCIAL EFFECTS</u>: On the positive side, a new theme park will provide <u>jobs for locals</u> and <u>entertainment</u> for the area. It will <u>attract tourists</u> who will spend money in local businesses. On the downside, there will be an increase in <u>traffic</u>, <u>noise</u> and <u>litter</u>.

Revise roller coasters — don't let your thoughts wander off into oblivion...

Roller coasters are constantly transferring between <u>potential and kinetic energy</u>. In reality, energy will be lost due to friction, air resistance and even as sound. But in exams you can usually ignore those.

Einstein's Relativity

Einstein's relativity is probably the most famous theory in physics, but it took years to be accepted.

Einstein Used Thought Experiments to Help Develop His Ideas

1) There are two ways in which <u>theories</u> can develop — some are based on <u>experimental results</u>, but others come about through <u>reasoning</u> and <u>creative thinking</u>. <u>Einstein's theory of relativity</u> is a good example of a theory that's based on theoretical ideas, not experimentation.

2) Einstein published his <u>special theory of relativity</u> in 1905. It was based on just a couple of simple assumptions, one of which was that the <u>speed of light</u>, <u>relative</u> to you, is <u>always the same</u>, no matter how fast you're going and in what direction. (And that's a wee bit weird when you think about it.)

3) He developed his ideas through <u>thought experiments</u>. A thought experiment is a way of looking at an abstract idea by creating a <u>hypothetical problem</u> and using <u>reasoning</u> to solve it, e.g. "What'd happen to time in a ship travelling at close to the speed of light?" Einstein used thought experiments a lot, often when it was impossible to do an actual experiment.

AMERICAN INSTITUTE OF PHYSICS / SCIENCE PHOTO LIBRARY

4) Einstein's theory was fairly <u>radical</u>. He predicted that <u>time and space</u> aren't <u>fixed</u> — they can both <u>stretch or shrink</u> depending on how you're moving.

5) He extended his ideas in 1915 with his <u>general</u> theory of relativity. One of the predictions from this theory was that <u>gravity</u> would <u>bend light</u>.

6) These ideas were a bit too <u>controversial</u> for many to accept at the time, because they contradicted Newton's laws of motion.

Scientists Can be a Bit Set in Their Ways

1) Scientists can be <u>reluctant</u> to accept new theories, especially if they challenge the established way of thinking. <u>Newton's laws of motion</u> predicted that the speed of a ray of light, relative to you, should depend on your velocity — just like the speed of everything else. These laws had stood for over 200 years, so when Einstein came along and questioned them it was a <u>big deal</u>.

2) A radical theory like this is much more likely to be accepted if it's the work of <u>more than one</u> person. Makes sense if you think about it — the theory can't really be dismissed as one person's crazy idea.

3) Before Einstein's theory was published, several <u>other scientists</u> were already working in similar areas.

4) In the 1880s, two American physicists, <u>Albert Michelson</u> and <u>Edward Morley</u>, carried out experiments that suggested that the speed of light was always the same. And the Dutch physicist <u>Hendrik Lorentz</u> had already produced work on the effect of motion on space and time.

5) <u>Observations</u> which support a theory can greatly increase its chances of acceptance, e.g. observations made during a <u>solar eclipse in 1919</u> supported Einstein's prediction that light is bent by gravity.

A Good Theory Should Make Predictions That Can be Tested

1) Einstein's theories made <u>very precise predictions</u> about the effects of motion on time.

2) These predictions couldn't be <u>tested</u> for <u>many years</u> because our equipment wasn't accurate enough.

3) However, once testing did become possible, his predictions worked in <u>many different situations</u>, e.g.

<u>ATOMIC CLOCKS</u> — Scientists flew atomic clocks in a plane around the world and measured the time taken. The time measured by the moving clocks was very slightly different from that measured by stationary clocks on the ground. It appeared that time passed <u>more slowly</u> on the moving plane.

<u>COSMIC RAYS</u> — Cosmic rays can produce very short-lived particles called muons. When muons are moving at close to the speed of light, their lifetime seems to increase, i.e. time moves more slowly for them.

Special relativity — that's why time goes faster in exams...

This page is about <u>scientific theories</u>, how they are developed, and what determines whether they are accepted. Even if they are accepted, it doesn't mean they can't be <u>challenged</u> at some point in the future.

Revision Summary for P2 Topic 10

Well this section sure is a roller coaster of emotions — it starts off with some fairly mundane stuff about energy, moves on to race tracks and looping the loop, and finally ends up with one of the most famous theories in physics — Einstein's relativity. Phew. I'd better leave you a minute to recover...

... OK then, time to answer some questions. The ones below, to be precise. They shouldn't take long if you know your stuff. Keep going until you can answer them all.

1)   What's the connection between 'work done' and 'energy transferred'?

2)* Write down the formula for work done. A crazy dog drags a big branch 12 m over the next-door neighbour's front lawn, pulling with a force of 535 N. How much energy is transferred?

3)* What's the formula for kinetic energy? Find the kinetic energy of a 78 kg sheep moving at 23 m/s. If the sheep increases its speed to 30 m/s, does it have more or less kinetic energy?

4)   Write down the formula for electrical energy.

5)* An electric kettle draws a current of 12 A from the 230 V mains supply. Calculate the energy transferred by the kettle in 1 minute.

6)* Write down the formula for gravitational potential energy. Calculate the increase in potential energy when a box of mass 12 kg is raised through 4.5 m.

7)* A roller coaster train of mass 15 000 kg starts from the top of a hill. As it travels down the hill it drops a vertical distance of 50 m. How much potential energy does it lose in this time?

8)   Write down the principle of the conservation of energy.

9)* Assuming no air resistance, calculate the kinetic energy of a 78 kg sheep just as it hits the floor after falling from a height of 20 m. How fast is the sheep travelling as it hits the floor?

10) What's the formula for power? What are the units of power?

11)* An electric motor transfers 540 kJ of electrical energy in 4½ minutes. What is its power output?

12)* Calculate the power output of a 78 kg sheep which runs 20 m up a staircase in 16.5 seconds.

13) Name three forces that can provide a centripetal force.

14) A cyclist is moving at a constant speed of 5 m/s around a circular track of radius 20 m.
    a) Is the cyclist accelerating? Explain your answer.
    b) What force keeps the cyclist travelling in a circle? Where does this force come from?
    c)* Calculate the size of the force if the combined mass of the cyclist and her bike is 80 kg.
    d) What will happen to the size of this force if the same cyclist travels at a constant speed of 5 m/s around a different circular track that has a larger radius?

15)* At the top of a roller coaster ride a carriage has 150 kJ of gravitational P.E. Ignoring friction, how much K.E. will the carriage have at the bottom (where P.E. = 0)?

16)* A roller coaster is travelling at a speed of 40 m/s. What's the maximum height it could climb to if all its kinetic energy is transferred to gravitational potential energy?

17) Jim is in a roller coaster carriage going through a circular loop.
    a) In what direction is there a resultant force acting on Jim?
    b) Where is this force coming from?
    c) At the top of the loop Jim momentarily feels weightless. Explain why.

18) State two safety features associated with theme park rides.

19) Give one positive effect and one negative effect on the local area of building a new theme park.

20) Describe two ways in which new scientific theories can emerge.

21) How did Einstein use thought experiments?

22) Scientists were reluctant to accept Einstein's theory of relativity when it was first published. Explain why, and suggest two things that helped to get the theory accepted eventually.

* Take g = 10 m/s². Answers on page 106.

Ionising Radiation

Ionisation is where an atom either loses or gains electrons. There are three types of ionising radiation...

Ionising Radiation: Alpha, Beta and Gamma (α, β and γ)

You need to remember three things about each type of radiation:

1) What it actually is.
2) How strongly it ionises a material (i.e. bashes into atoms and knocks electrons off).
3) How well it penetrates materials.

There's a pattern: The more ionising the radiation is, the less penetrating it is. Particles of strongly ionising radiation collide with lots of atoms and knock electrons off. This activity means they give up their kinetic energy more quickly — so don't penetrate far into materials.

Alpha Particles are Helium Nuclei $\quad {}^{4}_{2}He$

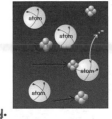

1) They are relatively big and heavy and slow-moving.
2) They have a strong positive charge (see p.95).
3) Their big mass and charge make them strongly ionising. This just means they bash into lots of atoms and knock electrons off them, which creates lots of ions — hence the term 'ionising'. So they don't penetrate far into materials, but are stopped quickly.

Beta Particles are Electrons $\quad {}^{0}_{-1}e$

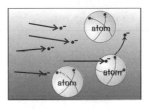

1) These are in between alpha and gamma in terms of their properties.
2) They move quite fast and they are quite small (they're electrons).
3) They have a negative charge (see p.95).
4) They are moderately ionising and penetrate moderately before colliding.
5) For every β-particle emitted, a neutron turns to a proton in the nucleus.

Gamma Rays are Very Short Wavelength EM Waves

1) They are the opposite of alpha particles in a way.
2) They tend to pass through rather than collide with atoms, so they are weakly ionising and can penetrate a long way into materials. Eventually they hit something and do damage.

Gamma rays and X-rays are very similar, and have very similar properties. The only real difference between them is in the way they're produced. X-rays can be made by firing electrons at a piece of metal. Gamma rays are released from unstable atomic nuclei when they decay.

Remember What Blocks the Three Types of Radiation...

They really like this for exam questions, so make sure you know what it takes to block each of the three:

Alpha particles are blocked by paper.
Beta particles are blocked by thin aluminium.
Gamma rays are blocked by thick lead.
Of course anything equivalent will also block them, e.g. skin will stop alpha, but not the others; a thin sheet of any metal will stop beta; and very thick concrete will stop gamma just like lead does.

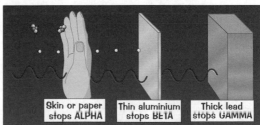

Skin or paper stops ALPHA | Thin aluminium stops BETA | Thick lead stops GAMMA

Don't let alpha particles upset you — be a bit more thick-skinned...

The different properties of these types of radiation are what make them suitable for different purposes. For example, alpha particles are used in smoke detectors but you wouldn't want them sterilising your food. I'm afraid you'll have to wait a while for more on the uses of radiation (ooh, I'm such a tease).

Background Radiation

We're constantly exposed to <u>very low levels</u> of radiation — and all without us noticing. Sneaky.

Background Radiation Comes from Many Sources

Background radiation comes from:

1) Radioactivity of naturally occurring <u>unstable isotopes</u> which are <u>all around us</u> — in the <u>air</u>, in <u>food</u>, in <u>building materials</u> and in the <u>rocks</u> under our feet.

2) Radiation from <u>space</u>, which is known as <u>cosmic rays</u>. These come mostly from the <u>Sun</u>. Luckily, the Earth's <u>atmosphere protects</u> us from much of this radiation. The Earth's <u>magnetic field</u> also deflects cosmic rays away from Earth.

3) Radiation due to <u>human activity</u>, e.g. <u>fallout</u> from <u>nuclear explosions</u> or <u>dumped nuclear waste</u>. But this represents a <u>tiny</u> proportion of the total background radiation.

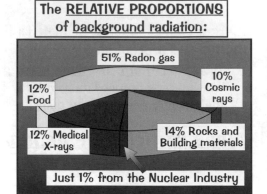

The **RELATIVE PROPORTIONS** of <u>background radiation</u>:

51% Radon gas

10% Cosmic rays

12% Food

12% Medical X-rays

14% Rocks and Building materials

Just 1% from the Nuclear Industry

The Level of Background Radiation Changes Depending on Where You Are

1) At <u>high altitudes</u> (e.g. in <u>jet planes</u>) it <u>increases</u> because of more exposure to <u>cosmic rays</u>. That means commercial pilots have an increased risk of getting some types of cancer (see p.99).

2) <u>Underground in mines</u>, etc. it increases because of the <u>rocks</u> all around.

3) Certain <u>underground rocks</u> (e.g. granite) can cause higher levels at the <u>surface</u>, especially if they release <u>radioactive radon gas</u>, which tends to get <u>trapped inside people's houses</u>.

Radon Gas is the Subject of Scientific Debate

1) The <u>radon concentration</u> in people's houses <u>varies widely</u> across the UK, depending on what type of <u>rock</u> the house is built on.

2) Studies have shown that exposure to <u>high doses</u> of radon gas can cause <u>lung cancer</u> (see p.99) — and the <u>greater</u> the radon concentration, the <u>higher the risk</u>.

3) The scientific community is a bit divided on the effects of <u>lower doses</u>, and there's still a lot of debate over what the highest safe(ish) concentration is.

4) Evidence suggests that the risk of developing lung cancer from radon is <u>much greater</u> for <u>smokers</u> compared to non-smokers.

5) Some medical professionals reckon that about <u>1 in 20</u> deaths from <u>lung cancer</u> (about 2000 per year) are caused by radon exposure.

6) <u>New houses</u> in areas where high levels of radon gas might occur must be designed with <u>good ventilation systems</u>. These reduce the concentration of radon in the living space.

7) In <u>existing houses</u>, the Government recommends that ventilation systems are put in wherever the radon concentration is higher than a certain level.

Millom

Coloured bits indicate more radiation from rocks

Background radiation — it's like nasty wallpaper...

Did you know that background radiation was first discovered <u>accidentally</u>. Scientists were trying to work out which materials were radioactive, and couldn't understand why their reader still showed radioactivity, when there was <u>no material</u> being tested. They realised it must be natural background radiation.

Atomic Structure

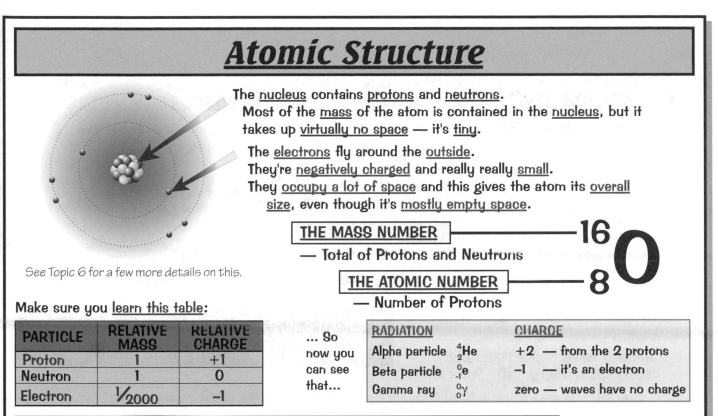

The <u>nucleus</u> contains <u>protons</u> and <u>neutrons</u>.
Most of the <u>mass</u> of the atom is contained in the <u>nucleus</u>, but it takes up <u>virtually no space</u> — it's <u>tiny</u>.

The <u>electrons</u> fly around the <u>outside</u>.
They're <u>negatively charged</u> and really really <u>small</u>.
They <u>occupy a lot of space</u> and this gives the atom its <u>overall size</u>, even though it's <u>mostly empty space</u>.

THE MASS NUMBER ———————— 16

— Total of Protons and Neutrons

THE ATOMIC NUMBER ————— 8

— Number of Protons

$^{16}_{8}\text{O}$

See Topic 6 for a few more details on this.

Make sure you <u>learn this table</u>:

PARTICLE	RELATIVE MASS	RELATIVE CHARGE
Proton	1	+1
Neutron	1	0
Electron	1/2000	−1

… So now you can see that…

RADIATION		CHARGE
Alpha particle	$^{4}_{2}\text{He}$	+2 — from the 2 protons
Beta particle	$^{0}_{-1}\text{e}$	−1 — it's an electron
Gamma ray	$^{0}_{0}\gamma$	zero — waves have no charge

Isotopes are Different Forms of the Same Element

1) <u>Isotopes</u> are atoms with the <u>same</u> number of <u>protons</u> but a <u>different</u> number of <u>neutrons</u>.
2) Hence they have the <u>same atomic (proton) number</u>, but <u>different mass (nucleon) numbers</u>.
3) <u>Carbon-12</u> and <u>carbon-14</u> are good examples:
4) <u>Most elements</u> have different isotopes, but there's usually only one or two <u>stable</u> ones.
5) The other isotopes tend to be <u>radioactive</u>, which means they <u>decay</u> into <u>other elements</u> and <u>give out radiation</u>. This is where all <u>radioactivity</u> comes from — <u>unstable</u> radioactive isotopes undergoing <u>nuclear decay</u> and spitting out <u>high-energy particles</u> or <u>waves</u>.

$^{12}_{6}\text{C}$ $^{14}_{6}\text{C}$

two extra neutrons

Radioactivity is a Totally Random Process

<u>Unstable nuclei</u> will <u>decay</u> and in the process <u>give out radiation</u>. This process is entirely <u>random</u>. This means that if you have 1000 unstable nuclei, you can't say when <u>any one of them</u> is going to decay, and neither can you do anything at all <u>to make a decay happen</u>.
Each nucleus will just decay quite <u>spontaneously</u> in its <u>own good time</u>. It's completely unaffected by <u>physical</u> conditions like <u>temperature</u> or by any sort of <u>chemical bonding</u> etc.

When the nucleus <u>does</u> decay it will <u>spit out</u> one or more of the three types of radiation, <u>alpha</u>, <u>beta</u> or <u>gamma</u>, and in the process the <u>nucleus</u> will often <u>change</u> into a <u>new element</u>:

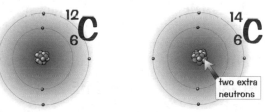

You can write these decays as <u>nuclear equations</u>. Watch out for the <u>mass and atomic numbers</u> — they have to <u>balance up</u> on both sides…

E.g. $^{238}_{92}\text{U} \rightarrow ^{234}_{90}\text{Th} + ^{4}_{2}\text{He} + ^{0}_{0}\gamma$ $238 \rightarrow 234 + 4 + 0$
$92 \rightarrow 90 + 2 + 0$

$^{14}_{6}\text{C} \rightarrow ^{14}_{7}\text{N} + ^{0}_{-1}\text{e}$ $14 \rightarrow 14 + 0$
$6 \rightarrow 7 + (-1)$

Completely random — just like your revision shouldn't be…

It's the number of <u>protons</u> which decides what <u>element</u> something is, then the number of <u>neutrons</u> decides what <u>isotope</u> of that element it is. And it's <u>unstable isotopes</u> which undergo <u>radioactive decay</u>.

Half-Life

The Radioactivity of a Sample Always Decreases Over Time

1) This is <u>pretty obvious</u> when you think about it. Each time a <u>decay</u> happens and an alpha, beta or gamma is given out, it means one more <u>radioactive nucleus</u> has <u>disappeared</u>.

2) Obviously, as the <u>unstable nuclei</u> all steadily disappear, the <u>activity as a whole</u> will <u>decrease</u>. So the <u>older</u> a sample becomes, the <u>less radiation</u> it will emit.

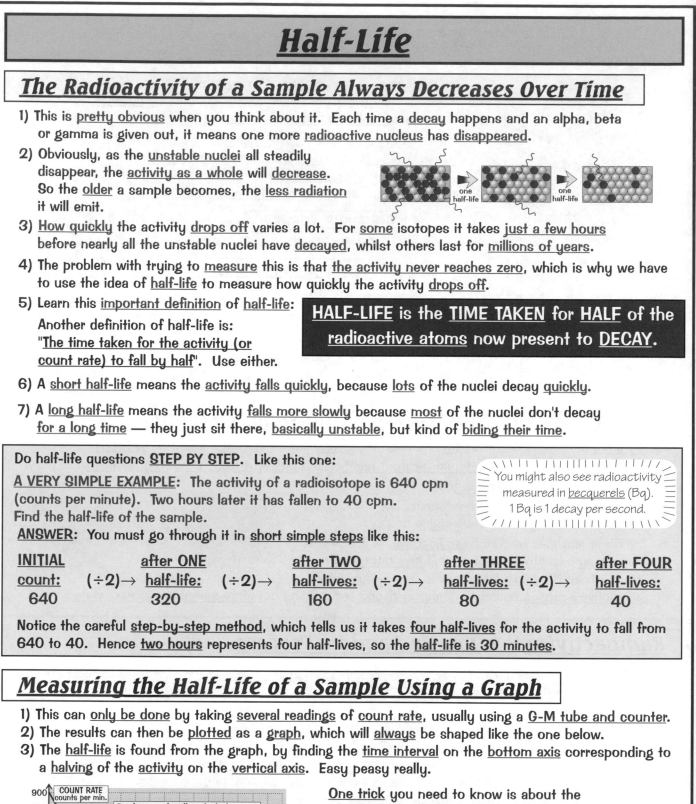

3) <u>How quickly</u> the activity <u>drops off</u> varies a lot. For <u>some</u> isotopes it takes <u>just a few hours</u> before nearly all the unstable nuclei have <u>decayed</u>, whilst others last for <u>millions of years</u>.

4) The problem with trying to <u>measure</u> this is that <u>the activity never reaches zero</u>, which is why we have to use the idea of <u>half-life</u> to measure how quickly the activity <u>drops off</u>.

5) Learn this <u>important definition</u> of <u>half-life</u>:

Another definition of half-life is: "<u>The time taken for the activity (or count rate) to fall by half</u>". Use either.

> **HALF-LIFE** is the **TIME TAKEN** for **HALF** of the <u>radioactive atoms</u> now present to **DECAY**.

6) A <u>short half-life</u> means the <u>activity falls quickly</u>, because <u>lots</u> of the nuclei decay <u>quickly</u>.

7) A <u>long half-life</u> means the activity <u>falls more slowly</u> because <u>most</u> of the nuclei don't decay <u>for a long time</u> — they just sit there, <u>basically unstable</u>, but kind of <u>biding their time</u>.

Do half-life questions **STEP BY STEP**. Like this one:

A VERY SIMPLE EXAMPLE: The activity of a radioisotope is 640 cpm (counts per minute). Two hours later it has fallen to 40 cpm. Find the half-life of the sample.

> You might also see radioactivity measured in <u>becquerels</u> (Bq). 1 Bq is 1 decay per second.

ANSWER: You must go through it in <u>short simple steps</u> like this:

INITIAL count:		**after ONE half-life:**		**after TWO half-lives:**		**after THREE half-lives:**		**after FOUR half-lives:**
640	(÷2)→	320	(÷2)→	160	(÷2)→	80	(÷2)→	40

Notice the careful <u>step-by-step method</u>, which tells us it takes <u>four half-lives</u> for the activity to fall from 640 to 40. Hence <u>two hours</u> represents four half-lives, so the <u>half-life is 30 minutes</u>.

Measuring the Half-Life of a Sample Using a Graph

1) This can <u>only be done</u> by taking <u>several readings</u> of <u>count rate</u>, usually using a <u>G-M tube and counter</u>.
2) The results can then be <u>plotted</u> as a <u>graph</u>, which will <u>always</u> be shaped like the one below.
3) The <u>half-life</u> is found from the graph, by finding the <u>time interval</u> on the <u>bottom axis</u> corresponding to a <u>halving</u> of the <u>activity</u> on the <u>vertical axis</u>. Easy peasy really.

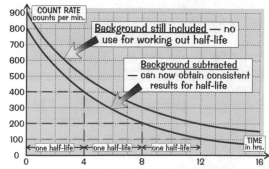

One trick you need to know is about the <u>background radiation</u>, which also enters the G-M tube and gives <u>false readings</u>. Measure the background count <u>first</u> and then <u>subtract it</u> from <u>every reading</u> you get, before plotting the results on the <u>graph</u>. Realistically, the <u>only difficult bit</u> is actually <u>remembering</u> about that for your <u>exam</u>, should they ask you about it. They could also test that idea in a <u>calculation question</u>.

Half-life of a box of chocolates — about five minutes...

You can produce more accurate graphs of half-life by using <u>computer software</u> (see page 98).

Uses of Ionising Radiation

Smoke Detectors — Use α Radiation

1) A weak source of alpha radiation is placed in the detector, close to two electrodes.

2) The source causes ionisation, and a current flows.

3) If there is a fire then smoke will absorb the radiation — the current stops and the alarm sounds.

Tracers in Medicine — Always Short Half-Life γ-Emitters

1) Certain radioactive isotopes can be injected into people (or they can just swallow them) and their progress around the body can be followed using an external detector. A computer converts the reading to a display showing where the strongest reading is coming from.

2) A well-known example is the use of iodine-131, which is absorbed by the thyroid gland just like normal iodine-127, but it gives out radiation which can be detected to indicate whether the thyroid gland is taking in iodine as it should.

Gamma Rays

G-M tubes Ltd.

Iodine-131 collecting in the thyroid gland

3) All isotopes which are taken into the body must be GAMMA or BETA emitters (never alpha), so that the radiation passes out of the body — and they should only last a few hours, so that the radioactivity inside the patient quickly disappears (i.e. they should have a short half-life).

Radiotherapy — the Treatment of Cancer Using γ-Rays

1) Since high doses of gamma rays will kill all living cells, they can be used to treat cancers.

2) The gamma rays have to be directed carefully and at just the right dosage so as to kill the cancer cells without damaging too many normal cells.

3) However, a fair bit of damage is inevitably done to normal cells, which makes the patient feel very ill. But if the cancer is successfully killed off in the end, then it's worth it.

Sterilisation of Food and Surgical Instruments Using γ-Rays

1) Food can be exposed to a high dose of gamma rays which will kill all microbes, keeping the food fresh for longer.

2) Medical instruments can be sterilised in just the same way, rather than by boiling them.

3) The great advantage of irradiation over boiling is that it doesn't involve high temperatures, so things like fresh apples or plastic instruments can be totally sterilised without damaging them.

unsterilised — Gamma source — sterilised

4) The food is not radioactive afterwards, so it's perfectly safe to eat.

5) The isotope used for this needs to be a very strong emitter of gamma rays with a reasonably long half-life (at least several months) so that it doesn't need replacing too often.

Ionising radiation — just what the doctor ordered...

Radiation has many important uses — especially in medicine. Make sure you know why each application uses a particular isotope according to its half-life and the type of radiation it gives out.

Radioactive Dating

Radioactive Dating of Rocks and Archaeological Specimens

1) The discovery of radioactivity and the idea of half-life (see p.96) gave scientists their first opportunity to accurately work out the age of rocks, fossils and archaeological specimens.

2) By measuring the amount of a radioactive isotope left in a sample, and knowing its half-life, you can work out how long the thing has been around.

3) Igneous rocks contain radioactive uranium which has a ridiculously long half-life. It eventually decays to become stable isotopes of lead, so the big clue to a rock sample's age is the relative proportions of uranium and lead isotopes.

4) Igneous rock also contains the radioisotope potassium-40. It's decay produces stable argon gas and sometimes this gets trapped in the rock. Then it's the same process again — finding the relative proportions of potassium-40 and argon to work out the age.

Carbon-14 Calculations — Carbon Dating

ACTIVITY per g of carbon
(in counts per minute)

AGE (years)
5,000   10,000   15,000

1) Carbon-14 makes up about 1/10 000 000 (one ten-millionth) of the carbon in the air. This level stays fairly constant in the atmosphere.

2) The same proportion of C-14 is also found in living things.

3) However, when they die, the C-14 is trapped inside the wood or wool or whatever, and it gradually decays with a half-life of 5730 years.

4) So, by measuring the proportion of C-14 found in some old axe handle, burial shroud, etc. you can calculate how long ago the item was living material using the known half-life.

EXAMPLE:	An axe handle was found to contain 1 part in 40 000 000 C-14. How old is the axe?
ANSWER:	The C-14 was originally 1 part in 10 000 000. After one half-life it would be down to 1 part in 20 000 000. After two half-lives it would be down to 1 part in 40 000 000. Hence the axe handle is two C-14 half-lives old, i.e. 2 × 5730 = 11 460 years old.

The Results from Radioactive Dating aren't Perfect

Scientific conclusions are often full of uncertainties. This is because they're based on certain assumptions which may not always be true. For example, carbon dating is based on the following assumptions:

1) The level of C-14 in the atmosphere has always been constant.

2) All living things take in the same proportion of their carbon as C-14.

3) Substances haven't been contaminated by a more recent source of carbon (i.e. after they've died).

IN REALITY THOUGH...

1) The level of C-14 hasn't always been constant — cosmic radiation, climate change and human activity have all had an effect. To account for this, scientists adjust their results using calibration tables.

2) Not all living things act as we expect. For example, some plants take up less C-14 than expected — this means they seem older than they really are.

3) Scientists can't be 100% sure that a sample hasn't been contaminated.

MEASURING ERROR also affects the accuracy of results. The proportion of C-14 measured in a sample is unlikely to be exact — either because of the equipment used or human error.

When conducting scientific research, we can use technology to increase the accuracy of results. Measurements of radioactivity can be made more accurately by attaching the counter to a computer. Instead of taking readings and plotting a graph by hand, the computer's software plots the graph for you.

I tried dating rocks — they're not great for conversation...

Carbon dating was developed by Willard Libby in 1949. He came up with the original figure for C-14 half-life (5568 ± 30 years). It's now thought to be 5730 ± 40 years — this is known as the Cambridge half-life.

Radioactivity Safety

Attitudes towards the dangers of radioactivity changed a lot over the last century.

1) When Marie Curie discovered the radioactive properties of radium in 1898, nobody knew anything about its dangers. People were fascinated by radium — it was used in medicines and to make luminous paint. You could buy everyday products made using this paint, e.g. glow-in-the-dark watches.

2) However, by the 1930s people were starting to link health problems to radiation — many watch dial painters developed cancer as a result of exposure to radium. More recently, we've learnt a lot about the dangers of radiation from the long-term effects of terrible events like the nuclear attacks on Japan in 1945 and the Chernobyl disaster in 1986.

3) Nowadays there are strict rules governing the use of radioactive materials...

Radiation Harms Living Cells

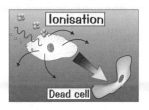

1) Alpha, beta and gamma radiation will cheerfully enter living cells and collide with molecules.

2) These collisions cause ionisation, which damages or destroys the molecules.

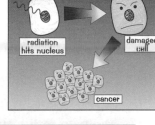

3) Lower doses tend to cause minor damage without killing the cell.

4) This can give rise to mutant cells which divide uncontrollably. This is cancer.

5) Higher doses tend to kill cells completely, which causes radiation sickness if a lot of body cells all get blatted at once.

6) The extent of the harmful effects depends on two things:
   a) How much exposure you have to the radiation.
   b) The energy and penetration of the radiation, since some types are more hazardous than others, of course.

Outside the Body, β- and γ-Sources are the Most Dangerous

This is because beta and gamma can get inside to the delicate organs, whereas alpha is much less dangerous because it can't penetrate the skin.

Inside the Body, an α-Source is the Most Dangerous

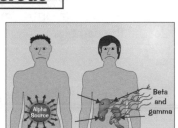

Inside the body alpha sources do all their damage in a very localised area. Beta and gamma sources on the other hand are less dangerous inside the body because they mostly pass straight out without doing much damage.

You Need to Learn About These Safety Precautions

Obviously radioactive materials need to be handled carefully. But in the exam they might ask you to list some specific precautions that should be taken when handling radioactive materials. If you want those easy marks you'd better learn all these:

In the School Laboratory:

1) Never allow skin contact with a source. Always handle with tongs.

2) Hold the source at arm's length to keep it as far from the body as possible.

3) Keep the source pointing away from the body and avoid looking directly at it.

4) Always store the source in a lead box and put it back in as soon as the experiment is over.

Radiation sickness — well yes, it does all get a bit tedious...

Sadly, much of our knowledge of the harmful effects of radiation has come as a result of devastating events such as the atomic bombing of Japan in 1945. In the months following the bombs, thousands suffered from radiation sickness — the symptoms of which include nausea, fatigue, skin burns, hair loss and, in serious cases, death. In the long term, the area has experienced increased rates of cancer, particularly leukaemia.

Revision Summary for P2 Topic 11

Hopefully those little radiation facts will have penetrated your brain and stored themselves away — ready to be emitted at high speed in the exam. But there's only one way to find out. And you know what that is, I'll bet. This page isn't full of questions for nothing. So off you go — write down the answers to all the questions, then go back over the section and see if there are any you got wrong. If so, read over the tricky bits and have another go at the questions. It's the best way to check you know your stuff.

1)   Describe in detail the nature and properties of the three types of ionising radiation: α, β and γ.

2)   Name a substance that will block each of the three types of nuclear radiation.

3)   What is the main difference between X-rays and gamma rays?

4)   Give three sources of background radiation.

5)   Describe how we are protected from much of the radiation from space.

6)   List three places where the level of background radiation is increased, and explain why.

7)   What feature must new houses in areas of high radon concentration be designed with?

8)   Sketch an atom. Give three details about the nucleus and the electrons.

9)   Draw a table stating the relative mass and charge of the three basic subatomic particles.

10)   Explain what the mass number and atomic number of an atom represent.

11)* Write down the number of protons and neutrons in an atom of $^{230}_{90}$Th.

12)   Explain what isotopes are. Give an example. Do stable or unstable isotopes undergo nuclear decay?

13)   Radioactivity is a totally random process. Explain what this means.

14)   Give a proper definition of half-life.

15)   Sketch a typical graph of activity against time. Show how you can find the half-life from your graph.

16)* The graph shows activity against time for a sample of radioactive material. Use the graph to find the half-life of the sample.

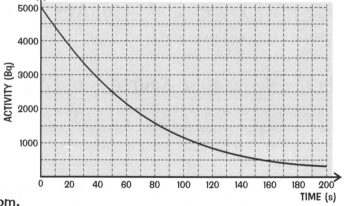

17)* The activity of a radioisotope is 840 cpm.
      Four hours later it has fallen to 105 cpm. Find the half-life of the sample.

18)   Describe in detail how radioactive sources are used in each of the following:
      a) smoke detectors,   c) sterilisation of food,
      b) tracers in medicine,   d) dating rocks.

19)* An old bit of cloth was found to have 1 atom of C-14 to 80 000 000 atoms of C-12.
      If C-14 decays with a half-life of 5730 years, and the proportion of C-14 to C-12 in living material is 1 to 10 000 000, find the age of the cloth.

20)   Why might you question your answer to question 18?

21)   Explain what kind of damage radiation causes to body cells. What are the effects of high doses? What damage do lower doses do?

22)   Which kinds of radioactive source are most dangerous: a) inside the body, b) outside the body?

23)   List four safety precautions that should be taken when handling radioactive materials in the school lab.

* Answers on page 106

Splitting the Atom

It's amazing how much <u>energy</u> there is <u>trapped</u> in a little atom. This energy is released by <u>nuclear fission</u>.

Scientists Use Theories to Make Predictions

1) As you saw in Topic 10 (page 91), scientists use <u>theories</u> to make <u>predictions</u> that can be tested. If these predictions are found to be <u>accurate</u>, they provide evidence to support the theory.

2) In his theory of <u>special relativity</u>, published in 1905, <u>Einstein</u> stated that there is an <u>equivalence</u> between mass and energy. This idea is summed up by his famous equation — $\underline{E = mc^2}$ (energy = mass × (speed of light)^2). Einstein predicted that <u>mass is a form of energy</u> — mass can be <u>converted into other forms of energy</u> and vice versa.

3) His predictions were <u>confirmed</u> over 30 years later by the development of <u>nuclear fission</u> (see below).

Nuclear Fission — The Splitting Up of Uranium Atoms

Nuclear fission uses the principle of <u>mass-energy equivalence</u> to release energy from uranium (or plutonium) atoms — either <u>peacefully</u> in nuclear reactors (see next page) or <u>destructively</u> in the form of a nuclear bomb. Both use the same <u>chain reaction</u>, but in a nuclear bomb the chain reaction is <u>uncontrolled</u>.

The Chain Reaction:

1) A <u>slow-moving neutron</u> is fired at the uranium-235 atom. The neutron is <u>absorbed</u> by the nucleus — this makes the atom unstable and causes it to split.

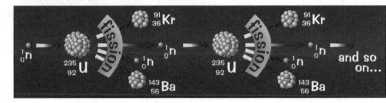

A neutron is <u>absorbed</u> by the nucleus because it has <u>no charge</u> — i.e. it's not <u>repelled</u> by the positive charge of the nucleus (see p.95 for more on charge).

2) When the U-235 atom splits it forms <u>two new lighter elements</u> ('daughter nuclei'). There are lots of different pairs of atoms that uranium can split into, e.g. krypton-91 and barium-143, but all these new nuclei are <u>radioactive</u> because they have the '<u>wrong</u>' number of neutrons in them.

3) Each time a <u>uranium</u> atom <u>splits up</u>, it also spits out <u>two or three neutrons</u>, which can hit <u>other</u> uranium nuclei, causing them to <u>split</u> also, and so on and so on. This is a <u>chain reaction</u>.

4) Each nucleus <u>splitting</u> (called a <u>fission</u>) gives out <u>a lot of energy</u>. Going back to Einstein's theory, this energy comes from the fact that the fission products have <u>slightly less mass</u> than the original nucleus — the 'lost' mass is <u>converted to energy</u>. Each fission gives out a lot more energy than you get with a <u>chemical</u> bond between two atoms. Make sure you remember that. <u>Nuclear processes</u> release <u>much more energy</u> than chemical processes do. That's why <u>nuclear bombs</u> are <u>so much</u> more powerful than ordinary bombs (which rely on <u>chemical</u> reactions).

Nuclear Fission Products are Radioactive

1) The daughter nuclei produced by nuclear fission have <u>too many neutrons</u> to be stable. To become more stable, they turn a <u>neutron</u> into a <u>proton</u> — giving off a <u>beta particle</u> at the same time.

2) This process continues, creating a <u>decay series</u>, until you get a <u>stable nucleus</u>.

3) Decay series are drawn with <u>arrows between each isotope</u> in the series, and show <u>what particle</u> each isotope emits when it decays, e.g. here are the decay series of <u>krypton-91</u> and <u>barium-143</u>:

$$^{91}Kr \xrightarrow{\beta^-} {}^{91}Rb \xrightarrow{\beta^-} {}^{91}Sr \xrightarrow{\beta^-} {}^{91}Y \xrightarrow{\beta^-} {}^{91}Zr \qquad \text{(stable zirconium-91)}$$

$$^{143}Ba \xrightarrow{\beta^-} {}^{143}La \xrightarrow{\beta^-} {}^{143}Ce \xrightarrow{\beta^-} {}^{143}Pr \xrightarrow{\beta^-} {}^{143}Nd \qquad \text{(stable neodymium 143)}$$

Don't know about you — but I fancy some fission chips...

When nuclear fission is used to produce energy in power stations, the chain reaction has to be <u>controlled</u> so that <u>safe</u> amounts of energy are released. This is done in a <u>nuclear reactor</u> (see next page). More of a problem are the <u>radioactive products</u> — these produce <u>ionising radiation</u>, so have to be disposed of safely...

Nuclear Power

Nuclear power stations use the energy released by nuclear fission (previous page) to generate electricity.

Nuclear Power Stations are Really Glorified Steam Engines

Nuclear power stations are powered by nuclear reactors. In a nuclear reactor, a controlled chain reaction takes place in which uranium atoms split up. The fission of an atom of uranium releases loads of energy, in the form of thermal energy (basically heat). This heat is used to boil water to drive a steam turbine.

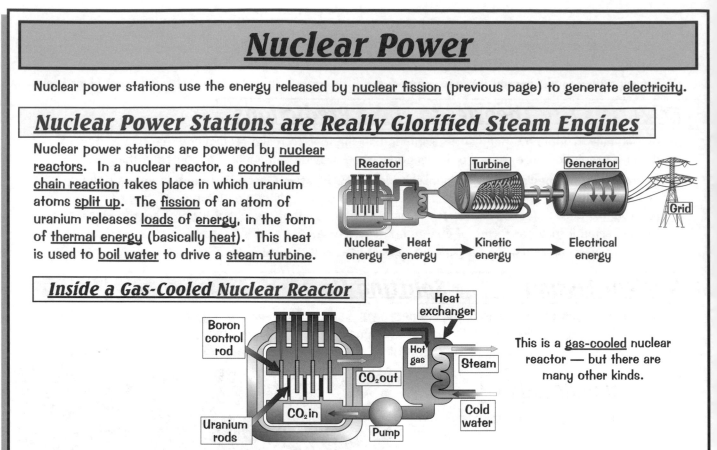

Inside a Gas-Cooled Nuclear Reactor

This is a gas-cooled nuclear reactor — but there are many other kinds.

1) Free neutrons in the reactor 'kick-start' the fission process.
2) The daughter products then collide with other atoms, causing the temperature in the reactor to rise.
3) Control rods, often made of boron, limit the rate of fission by absorbing excess neutrons.
4) A gas, typically carbon dioxide, is pumped through the reactor to carry away the heat generated.
5) The gas is then passed through a heat exchanger, where it gives its energy to water — this water is heated and turned into steam, which turns a turbine, generating electricity.

Using Nuclear Power Has Its Pros and Cons

1) Fossil fuels (coal, oil and gas) all release CO_2 when they're burnt. This adds to the greenhouse effect and global warming. Burning coal and oil also releases sulphur compounds that can cause acid rain.

2) In terms of emissions like these, nuclear power is very very clean.

3) The main environmental problem is with the disposal of waste. The products left over after nuclear fission are generally radioactive, so they can't just be thrown away.

4) There are a few ways to dispose of the waste. One way is to pack the waste into thick metal containers, put the containers in a very deep hole, then fill the hole with concrete.

5) Some of this waste will stay dangerously radioactive for hundreds of years, and some people worry that materials could leak out of the storage facilities over time.

6) And nuclear power always carries the risk of leaks from the plant or a major catastrophe like Chernobyl.

7) But it's not all doom and gloom. Building a nuclear plant can have a very positive impact on an area. Both the plant itself, and the support industries that spring up around it, bring lots of skilled jobs to rural areas like the west coast of Cumbria.

8) Nuclear fuel (i.e. the uranium) is cheap but the overall cost of nuclear power is high due to the cost of the power plant and final decommissioning. Dismantling a nuclear plant safely takes decades.

Revise nuclear power — full steam ahead...

Another way of dealing with high-level radioactive waste is to turn it into a more stable form. This can be done by melting the waste with certain materials to form glass — a process called vitrification. The liquid glass is poured into a stainless steel canister, which is welded shut, and then put into storage.

Nuclear Fusion

Loads of energy's released either when you break apart <u>really big nuclei</u> or join together <u>really small nuclei</u>. You can't do much with the ones in the middle, I'm afraid. (Don't ask, you don't want to know.)

Nuclear Fusion — The Joining of Small Atomic Nuclei

1) <u>Nuclear fusion</u> is the opposite of nuclear fission.
2) In nuclear fusion, two <u>light nuclei</u> (e.g. hydrogen) <u>combine</u> to create a larger nucleus.
3) Fusion releases <u>a lot</u> of energy (<u>more</u> than fission for a given mass) — all the energy released in <u>stars</u> comes from fusion. So people are trying to develop <u>fusion reactors</u> to make <u>electricity</u>.
4) Fusion <u>doesn't</u> leave behind a lot of radioactive <u>waste</u> and there's <u>plenty</u> of hydrogen knocking about to use as <u>fuel</u>.
5) The <u>big problem</u> is that fusion only happens at <u>really high densities and temperatures</u> (about <u>10 000 000 °C</u>).
6) <u>No material</u> can withstand that kind of temperature — it would just be <u>vaporised</u>, so fusion reactors are really hard to build.
7) You have to contain the hot hydrogen in a <u>magnetic field</u> instead of a physical container.
8) There are a few <u>experimental</u> reactors around at the moment, the biggest one being <u>JET</u> (Joint European Torus), but none of them are generating electricity yet. It takes <u>more</u> power to get up to temperature than the reactor can produce.

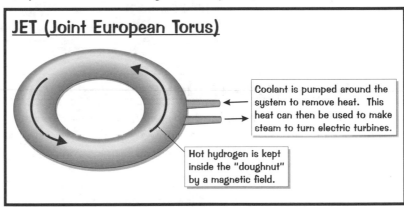

JET (Joint European Torus)

Coolant is pumped around the system to remove heat. This heat can then be used to make steam to turn electric turbines.

Hot hydrogen is kept inside the "doughnut" by a magnetic field.

Cold Fusion — Hoax or Energy of the Future?

1) A new scientific theory has to go through a <u>validation</u> process before it's accepted. This means making the <u>research results public</u> — usually in a <u>journal</u> such as <u>Nature</u>, so that other scientists can <u>repeat</u> the experiments. If lots of scientists get the <u>same results</u>, the theory is likely to be <u>accepted</u>.
2) An example of a theory which <u>hasn't</u> been accepted yet is '<u>cold fusion</u>'. Cold fusion is <u>nuclear fusion</u> which occurs at around <u>room temperature</u>, rather than at millions of degrees Celsius.
3) In 1989 two scientists, <u>Stanley Pons</u> and <u>Martin Fleischmann</u>, reported to a press conference that they had succeeded in releasing energy from cold fusion, using a simple experiment. This caused a lot of <u>excitement</u> — cold fusion would make it possible to generate lots of electricity, easily and cheaply. However, many scientists were <u>sceptical</u>, believing that fusion is only possible at very high temperatures.
4) After the press conference, other scientists tried to <u>repeat</u> Pons and Fleichmann's work. But <u>few</u> managed to reproduce the results <u>reliably</u>. When a group at <u>MIT</u> (Massachusetts Institute of Technology) <u>discredited</u> the theory, the feeling against cold fusion was so strong that some scientific journals <u>refused to publish</u> papers on it.
5) Despite all the setbacks, there is still <u>funding</u> available for cold fusion research, and Pons and Fleichmann's results have actually been <u>repeated</u> many times now — although <u>not reliably enough</u> for the theory to be accepted by the scientific community.

Pity they can't release energy by confusion...*

At about the same time as research started on fusion reactors, physicists were working on a <u>fusion bomb</u>. These "hydrogen bombs" are incredibly powerful — they can release a few thousand times more energy than the nuclear bombs that destroyed Hiroshima and Nagasaki at the end of World War II.

*There'd be plenty of physics books to use as fuel.

Static Electricity

Static electricity is all about charges which are <u>not</u> free to move. This causes them to build up in one place and it often ends with a <u>spark</u> or a <u>shock</u> when they do finally move.

1) <u>Build-up of Static is Caused by Friction</u>

1) When two <u>insulating</u> materials are <u>rubbed</u> together, electrons will be <u>scraped off one</u> and <u>dumped</u> on the other.

2) This'll leave a <u>positive</u> static charge on one and a <u>negative</u> static charge on the other.

3) <u>Which way</u> the electrons are transferred <u>depends</u> on the <u>two materials</u> involved.

4) Electrically charged objects <u>attract</u> small objects placed near them.
(Try this: rub a balloon on a woolly pully — then put it near tiddly bits of paper and watch them jump.)

5) The classic examples are <u>polythene</u> and <u>acetate</u> rods being rubbed with a <u>cloth duster</u>, as shown in the diagrams.

> With the <u>polythene rod</u>, electrons move <u>from the duster</u> to the rod.

> With the <u>acetate rod</u>, electrons move <u>from the rod</u> to the duster.

2) <u>Only Electrons Move — Never the Positive Charges</u>

<u>Watch out for this in exams</u>. Both +ve and −ve electrostatic charges are only ever produced by the movement of <u>electrons</u>. The positive charges <u>definitely do not move</u>. A positive static charge is always caused by electrons <u>moving</u> away elsewhere, as shown above. Don't forget!

A charged conductor can be <u>discharged safely</u> by connecting it to earth with a <u>metal strap</u> — this is called <u>earthing</u>. The electrons flow <u>down</u> the strap to the ground if the charge is <u>negative</u> and flow <u>up</u> the strap from the ground if the charge is <u>positive</u>.

3) <u>Like Charges Repel, Opposite Charges Attract</u>

This is <u>easy</u> and, I'd have thought, <u>kind of obvious</u>.
Two things with <u>opposite</u> electric charges are <u>attracted</u> to each other.
Two things with the <u>same</u> electric charge will <u>repel</u> each other.
These forces get <u>weaker</u> the <u>further apart</u> the two things are.

4) <u>As Charge Builds Up, So Does the Voltage — Causing Sparks</u>

The greater the <u>charge</u> on an <u>isolated</u> object, the greater the <u>voltage</u> between it and the Earth. If the voltage gets <u>big enough</u>, a <u>spark</u> will <u>jump</u> across the gap. High voltage cables can be <u>dangerous</u> for this reason. Big sparks have been known to <u>leap</u> from <u>overhead cables</u> to earth. But not often.

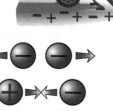

'ZAP!'

<u>Static caravans — where electrons go on holiday...</u>

Static electricity's great fun. You must have tried it — rubbing a balloon against your jumper and trying to get it to stick to the ceiling. It really works... well, sometimes. Bad hair days are caused by static too — it builds up on your hair, so your strands of hair repel each other. Which is nice...

Static Electricity — Examples

Static Electricity Being Helpful:

1) Fingerprinting

1) <u>Static</u> can be used by forensic scientists to take <u>fingerprints</u> from a crime scene.

2) A <u>fine dust</u> is brushed over surfaces, which sticks to the ridges of a fingerprint.

3) This dust can then be picked up using an <u>electrostatic dust-lifter</u>.

4) A <u>thin film</u> is given a high <u>positive charge</u> and pressed down onto the dust. The tiny dust particles are <u>attracted</u> to the charged surface and leave an <u>impression</u> of the print on the film.

5) Dust-lifters can also be used to pick up <u>dusty footprints</u> and <u>tyre marks</u>.

2) Laser Printing

1) Using <u>coded</u> information from a computer, a <u>laser beam</u> scans across the <u>positively charged</u> rotating <u>drum</u>.

2) Where the laser hits the drum the electrical charge is <u>removed</u>. This creates an <u>image</u> of the page on the drum.

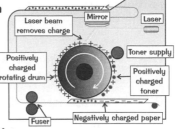

3) <u>Positively charged toner</u> is then applied to the drum. This black powder clings to the <u>discharged</u> areas of the drum, and is repelled from the rest of it.

4) As the drum rolls over the <u>negatively charged</u> sheet of paper, the <u>powder</u> is attracted to the paper, and the paper picks up the <u>image</u>.

5) The paper passes through the <u>fuser</u> — heated rollers which melt the powder, forming permanent <u>print</u>.

Static Electricity Being a Little Joker:

1) Clothing Crackles

When <u>synthetic clothes</u> are <u>dragged</u> over each other (like in a <u>tumble drier</u>) or over your <u>head</u>, electrons get scraped off, leaving <u>static charges</u> on both parts, and that leads to the inevitable — <u>attraction</u> (they stick together) and little <u>sparks</u> as the charges <u>rearrange themselves</u>.

2) Car Shocks

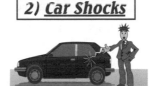

Static charge can also build up between your <u>clothes</u> and a synthetic <u>car seat</u>. Then, when you get out of the car and touch the <u>metal door</u> it can give you a real 'buzz'. Some cars have <u>conducting rubber strips</u> which hang down behind the car. This gives a <u>safe discharge</u> to earth.

Static Electricity Being Dangerous:

1) Lightning

Rain drops and ice <u>bump together</u> inside storm clouds, knocking off electrons and leaving the lower clouds <u>negatively charged</u>. This creates a <u>huge voltage</u> and a <u>big spark</u>.

2) The Aircraft Fuelling Nightmare:

1) As <u>fuel</u> flows out of the <u>fuel pipe</u> the fuel gains electrons from the pipe, giving it a <u>–ve</u> charge and the pipe a <u>+ve</u> charge.

2) The <u>voltage</u> between the fuel and the pipe can easily lead to a <u>spark</u>, which could ignite the fuel... <u>BOOM!</u>

3) <u>The solution</u>: connect the plane fuel tank to earth with a <u>metal strap</u> so that the charge is <u>conducted away</u>, instead of building up. OR connect the <u>fuel tanker</u> and the <u>plane</u> by a metal conductor.

More static electricity — it's shocking stuff...

Lightning always chooses the <u>easiest path</u> to get to the ground — even if that means going through tall buildings and trees. That's why you should never put up an umbrella or fly a kite in a thunderstorm.

Revision Summary for P2 Topic 12

What d'you know, we've reached the end of the book... well almost — just a few questions to do first. There's some tricky physics in this section — and strange ideas like 'mass is energy', which take a bit of getting used to. On the upside there are only five pages to learn, so just take it slowly. When you're ready, have a go at these little beauties. Keep going till you've got every single one.

1) What principle does nuclear fission use to release energy? Who came up with this principle?

2) What type of particle is U-235 bombarded with to make it split?

3) Draw a diagram to illustrate the fission of uranium-235 and explain how the chain reaction works.

4) What type of radiation do fission daughter products give out?

5)* Here is the decay series for krypton-91 with some bits missing: $^{91}Kr \xrightarrow{?} {}^{?}Rb \xrightarrow{?} {}^{?}Sr \xrightarrow{?} {}^{?}Y \xrightarrow{?} {}^{?}Zr$
Write out the series, filling in the missing bits.

6) Explain in terms of energy transfers how electricity is produced in a nuclear power station.

7) What are used in a nuclear reactor to slow down neutrons which are moving too quickly?

8) Give one reason for using nuclear power rather than fossil fuels.

9) What is the main environmental problem associated with nuclear power?

10) What is nuclear fusion? Why is it difficult to construct a working fusion reactor?

11) Which releases more energy for a given mass — fusion or fission?

12) Describe the process that new scientific theories have to go through before they are accepted.

13) What is 'cold fusion'? Why are many scientists still sceptical about cold fusion as a way of releasing energy?

14) What is static electricity? What causes it to build up?

15) Which particles move when static builds up? Which particles don't move?

16) How can a charged conductor be discharged? What is this process called?

17) What causes sparks?

18) Give two examples of how static electricity can be helpful. Write all the details.

19) Give two examples each of static electricity being: a) a nuisance, b) dangerous.

20) Explain why taking a woolly hat off can make your hair stand on end.

* Answer below

Physics Answers

P106 Revs: 5) $^{91}Kr \xrightarrow{\beta} {}^{91}Rb \xrightarrow{\beta} {}^{91}Sr \xrightarrow{\beta} {}^{91}Y \xrightarrow{\beta} {}^{91}Zr$

P2 Topic 12

19) 17 190 years old

17) 80 minutes

16) 50 seconds

P100 Revs: 11) 90 protons and 140 neutrons

P2 Topic 11

16) 80 m

15) 150 kJ

14 c) 100 N

12) 945 W

11) 2000 W

9) K.E. = P.E. lost = 15 600 J; 20 m/s

7) 7 500 000 J

6) 540 J

5) 165 600 J

3) 20 631 J; more K.E.

P92 Revs: 2) 6420 J

P2 Topic 10

25) Shed 4

22) 700 N

20) 1170 kg m/s

14) 7.5 m/s²

5) 35 m/s²

3) No (speed = 12.6 m/s)

P84 Revs: 2) 0.091 m/s; 137 m

P2 Topic 9

Index

Symbols

3-dimensional models 62

_A_

abortion 11
acceleration 76-80, 89
acceleration of free-fall 86
acid rain 32
activation energy 69, 70
active transport 21
adaptation 28
adenine 4
aerobic respiration 1, 5, 6
agriculture 6
air bags 82
air pollution 30, 32, 34
air resistance 77, 78, 90
aircraft fuelling nightmare 105
alkali metals 54, 58
alkenes 40, 41, 43
alloys 59
alpha particles 93, 95, 97, 99
alternative fuels 39
amino acids 4
ammonia 22, 73
    ammonium nitrate fertiliser 73
anaerobic respiration 2, 5
anhydrous copper(II) sulphate 71
animal cells 18
animals 20, 23
anions 56, 60
anode 60
Antarctic 29
anthropogenic 31
antibiotics 5
aquaplaning 81
aqueous 38
Arctic 23
artificial hormones 13
artificial insemination 14
artificial selection 14
aseptic conditions 6
aspirin 45
athletes 2
atmosphere 18, 20, 22-24
    atmospheric temperature 31
atom economy 49
atomic (proton) number 52, 54, 95
atomic clocks 91
atoms 52
auxins 13

_B_

background radiation 94, 96
bacteria 5, 6, 22, 29
balancing equations 38
bases 4
beta particles
    93, 95, 97, 99, 101
binary salts 57
biodegradable plastics 43
biodiversity 35
biogas 18
biospheres 23
blood 1, 2
blood vessels 1
body temperature 2
bone marrow transplants 11
brakes 81
braking distance 81
breaking bonds 71

breathing rate 2
bromine water 40
buckminster fullerene 64

_C_

calculating masses 48
cancer 16, 94, 97
cancer cells 9
capillaries 1
car safety features 82
carbohydrates 6, 20
carbon 20, 24, 39, 40, 64
carbon cycle 20
carbon dioxide
    1, 5, 18, 19, 23, 24, 26, 30
carbon monoxide 30
carbon-12 95
carbon-14 95, 98
catalysts 67, 69, 70, 72
catalytic converters 30
cathode 60
cations 56, 60
cells 1, 2, 4, 5, 18, 97, 99
    cell division 9
    cell elongation 13
    cell membranes 18
    cell sap 18
    cells, mutant 99
    cellulose cell walls 18
centripetal forces 89, 90
CFCs 34
chain reaction 101
charge 95
chemosynthesis 29
chlorophyll 18, 19
chloroplasts 18
cholesterol 42
chromosomes 9, 10
circular motion 89
circulatory system 1
climate 6, 25
    climate change 24, 25, 30, 31
cloning 15
closed system 72
clothing 18
cold fusion 103
collision theory 69
combustion 20
competition 28, 29
concentration 67, 69
    concentration gradients 21
conduction, electrical 57, 59, 64
conduction, heat 59
conductor 104, 105
conservation 35
conservation of energy 87
construction materials 18
contamination 6
continuous variation 8
control groups 65
control rods 102
coppicing 35
cosmic rays 91, 94
covalent bonds 62, 63, 64
cracking 41
cramp 2
crash tests 82
crosslinks 44
crude oil 39
crumple zones 82
crystals 65

cultural heritage 35
culture medium 5, 6
current 86
Curie, Marie 99
cytoplasm 18
cytosine 4

_D_

decay 20
decay series 101
deceleration 76, 79
decomposers 22
deforestation 24, 30
denatured enzymes 70
denitrifying bacteria 22
diabetes 5
diamond 64
diets 3
differentiation 11
diffusion 1, 21
digital monitors 2
disease 5, 26
displacement 75
distance 75, 76
DNA 4, 5, 9, 15, 18
Dolly the sheep 15
double helix 4
drag 77, 78
droughts 25
drug development 45, 65
dry weight 8
dynamic equilibrium 72

_E_

Earth 18, 23, 24, 25, 26
earthing 104
eating 20
education 25
Einstein, Albert 91, 101
electrical energy 86
electricity, generating 102
electrolysis 60
electrolytes 60
electrons 52, 54-56, 58, 59, 93,
    95, 104
    electron configurations 55
    electron shells 55, 56, 58, 62
electrostatic charges 104, 105
electrostatic dust-lifter 105
empirical formulae 47
endangered species 35
endothermic reactions 71
energy 1, 2, 5, 24, 26, 85, 87
    energy flow 26
    energy loss 26
environmental conditions 19
enzymes 4-6, 19, 70
equilibrium 23
ethanol 39, 40
ethics 11, 25
eutrophication 21, 33, 73
exercise 2, 3
exothermic reactions 71, 73
extreme environments 29

_F_

F = ma 79, 80
falling objects 87
farming 14, 21, 24, 26
fats 3, 20
faulty genes 16
fermentation 5

fermenters 5, 6
fertilisers 21, 33, 73
fingerprinting 105
fish farms 26
Fleischmann, Martin 103
floods 25
foetal abnormality 11
food chains 20, 26
food production 26
food shortages 25
food supply 35
food surpluses 25
food web 28, 35
force diagrams 77
forces 77, 78, 79, 80, 82
forming bonds 71
fossil fuels 30, 32, 36
fossils 98
free-fallers 78
friction 89, 90, 77, 78
fuels 39
fullerenes 64
fungi 6

_G_

gametes 10, 11
gamma rays 93, 95, 97, 99
gas syringe 68
gene therapy 15, 16
genes 4, 5
genetic disorders 15, 16
genetic engineering 5
genetic modification 15
giant covalent structures 64
giant ionic structures 57
global warming 24, 25, 30
glow-in-the-dark watches 99
glucose 1, 2, 6, 18, 23, 26
graphite 64
gravitational force 89
gravitational potential energy
    86-88, 90
gravity 13, 77, 78
greenhouse gases 24
greenhouses 26
groups 54
growth 8, 26
    growth factors 8
guanine 4

_H_

Haber process 73
habitats 35
haemoglobin 29
haemophilia 5
half-equations 60
half-life 96-98
halogens 54, 58, 63
handling radioactive materials 99
Hayflick limit 9
hazards 81
health 3
heart disease 3
heart rate 2
heat exchanger 102
high altitudes 29
highway code 81
homeopathy 65
hospitals 97
human activities 28, 30
hurricanes 25

Index

hydration 40
hydrocarbons 40, 41
hydrogen 20
hydrogenation 42

I

indicator species 34
industrialisation 31
industry 6
inherited disorders 16
insulating materials 104
insulin 5
intensive farming methods 14
inter-molecular forces 63
interdependence 28
internal combustion engines 32
interpreting data 2, 31
ionic bonding 56, 57
ionisation 93, 99
ionising radiation 93
ions 56, 57, 60, 93
isotopes 53

J

JET (Joint European Torus) 103
jobs 25

K

kinetic energy 85, 87, 88, 90

L

lactic acid 2, 5
landfill sites 36
laser printing 105
lead 33
lichen 34
lift 77
light 19, 26
lightning 22, 105
limiting factors 19
living indicators 34
Lorentz, Hendrik 91
lungs 1

M

magnesium 21
magnetic bracelets 65
malleability 59
Mars 23
mass 79, 80, 82, 95
mass (nucleon) number 46, 52, 95
mass-energy equivalence 101
medicines 5, 18, 24
meiosis 10
metallic bonds 59
metals 59
methane 24
Michelson, Albert 91
microorganisms 5, 6, 20, 23
milk 5
minerals 6, 21
mitosis 9
molecular formulae 47
molecules 1, 5, 63
momentum 82
monomers 43
monounsaturated oils 42
Morley, Edward 91
muons 91
muscles 2
mutualistic relationships 22
mycoprotein 6

N

nanoparticles 64
nanotubes 64
natural disasters 25
natural variability 31
neutralisation 71
neutrons 52, 53, 95, 101, 102
nitrates 6, 12, 21, 22, 33, 73
nitrifying bacteria 22
nitrogen 5, 20, 22, 73
    nitrogen compounds 22
    nitrogen cycle 22
    nitrogen fixation 22
    nitrogen oxides 32
    nitrogen-fixing bacteria 22
noble gases 54, 58
nodules 22
nuclear bombs 101
nuclear decay 95, 96
nuclear equations 95
nuclear power 102
    nuclear fission 101, 102
    nuclear fusion 103
    nuclear waste 94
nuclei 52
nucleus 4, 18, 95
nutrients 20

O

oil 33
organelles 4
ova 10
over-fishing 35
oxygen 1, 2, 6, 18, 20, 22, 23
oxygen debt 2
ozone layer depletion 34

P

pain receptors 11
parachute 78
PCBs 33
penguins 29
penicillin 5
percentage yield 50
periodic table 54, 55
pesticides 26, 33
pests 25, 26
pH 6, 70
phosphates 12, 21, 33
photosynthesis 12, 18-20, 23, 24, 26
placebos 65
plants 1, 18, 20, 23
    plant cells 18
    plant growth 12, 13
    plant hormones 12, 13
plasticisers 44
plastics 43, 44
pollution 24, 30, 32
polymers 43, 44
polypeptides 4
polyunsaturated oils 42
Pons, Stanley 103
population 24
population size 28
potential energy 86-88, 90
poverty 25
power 88
precipitation 68
predation 28
predators 26
predictions 91

pregnancy 11
preservatives 44
pressure 67, 69, 72, 73
products 38
proteins 3-5, 20, 22
protons 52, 53, 95
purity 49
push or pull 77

R

radiation sickness 99
radioactivity 95-99
    radioactive isotopes 94-98
    radioactive waste 102
    radioactivity safety 99
radiocarbon dating 98
radium 99
radon gas 94
rates of reaction 67-69
raw materials 39, 49
raw sewage 21
reactants 38
reaction forces 77, 80, 90
reactivity trends 58
recycling 36, 43
refined sugars 3
reforestation 35
regeneration of parts of the body 8
relative abundances 53
relative atomic mass 46, 47, 53
relative formula mass 46, 48, 49
relativity 91, 101
resistance 78
respiration
    1, 2, 5, 6, 12, 18, 20, 21,
    23, 26
resultant force 77, 79
reversible reactions 50, 72
ribosomes 4
risk assessment 83
RNA 4
rocks 94, 98
roller coasters 90
root hairs 21

S

salmon farming 26
salt 3
saturated hydrocarbons 40
saturated oils 42
scientific conclusions 98
seat belts 82
seedless fruits 13
selective breeding 14
sewage 33
shielding 58
shocks 105
simple molecular substances 63
skin cancer 34
skydiver 77, 78
smoke detectors 97
soil 20-22
sparks 104, 105
speed 75, 76, 78
    speed cameras 75
    speed of light 91
sperm 10
stable communities 20
staged synthesis 45
standard of living 24
stars 103

state symbols 38
static electricity 104, 105
steady speed 77-79
stem cells 8, 9, 11
sterilisation of food and surgical
    instruments 97
stopping distance 81
subsidies 25
sulphur dioxide 32
surface area 21, 67, 69, 70

T

temperature 6, 19, 24, 67, 69-73
tension 89, 77
terminal velocity 77, 78
termination 11
territories 28
theme parks 90
theoretical yields 48
theories 91
thermal decomposition 41, 71
thermal energy 102
thermoplastic polymers 44
thermosetting polymers 44
thinking distance 81
thought experiments 91
thrust 77
thymine 4
time 75, 76
toxicity 45
tracers in medicine 97
trans fats 42
trees 24

U

unexpected reactions 50
unsaturated hydrocarbons 40
unsaturated oils 42
unstable isotopes 101
unstable nuclei 95, 96
ununquadium 54
uranium atoms 101, 102
UV radiation 34

V

vacuoles 18
velocity 75, 76, 82
velocity-time graphs 76
vitamins 6
volcanic vents 29
voltage 86, 104, 105

W

wars 25
waste 36, 49
waste products 20
water pollution 33
weight 77, 78, 80, 90
wet weight 8
wildlife 35
wood 18
woodland conservation 35
work 85
world economy 25
world food production 25

X

X-rays 93, 97

Y

yeast 5
yield 50